Ambition had killed Rachel Sims's and Christopher Blake's love ten years ago. Now, of course they were older and wiser, but was the maturity and strength of ten years of hurting enough to make this time more than a brief diplomatic affair?

Books you will enjoy
by CLAIRE HARRISON

AN INDEPENDENT WOMAN

Her disastrous affair with Douglas had taught
Jo a valuable lesson: independence is the only
guarantee of happiness. But, out in the clear
light of the Canadian Rockies, she began to
question certain aspects of her life, and Conrad
Wyatt made her wonder what 'independence'
really meant . . .

ONE LAST DANCE

Casmir Yakovaloskov, Marta Cole's virile
Russian ballet partner, was a threat to her
peace of mind. But it was not until she became
his partner off-stage as well as on that she
realised just how much of a threat he was . . .

DRAGON'S POINT

Maggie was convinced that nothing dangerous
could happen at Dragon's Point until Jason
Hale arrived, and she realised that there was
more than one kind of danger!

DIPLOMATIC AFFAIR

BY

CLAIRE HARRISON

MILLS & BOON LIMITED
15–16 BROOK'S MEWS
LONDON W1A 1DR

First published in Great Britain 1986
by Mills & Boon Limited

© Claire Harrison 1986

Australian copyright 1986
Philippine copyright 1986
This edition 1986

ISBN 0 263 75303 4

Set in Monophoto Times 10 on 10½ pt.
01–0386 – 56821

Made and printed in Great Britain by
Richard Clay (The Chaucer Press) Ltd,
Bungay, Suffolk

CHAPTER ONE

A tall, lean man with dark hair that glinted silver at the temples, dressed in a grey business suit, stood in the doorway of the library of the Canadian Embassy in Washington and had the odd feeling that ten years of his life had disappeared without a trace. It was all so very familiar; the wooden panelling, the draped flags, the pictures, and the books. Nothing had really changed; even the caterers who were so busy setting up a bar in one corner and decorating the long table down the middle looked much like those who had set up cocktail parties ten years before. The long, elegant room and the bustle of black-coated waiters took Christopher Blake back in time to those heady days when he was on his first foreign posting as First Secretary to the Minister.

He'd never thought then that one day he would return as Minister himself, second in command in the Embassy. His rise in the foreign service had been meteoric; two years in Paris, three in Mexico City, one year back in Ottawa and then three exhausting, intense years in Lebanon. External Affairs had brought him back, convinced that he'd needed to recuperate after living in war-torn Beirut, but Christopher had felt the usual restlessness in Ottawa. The Washington job had been the plum of this year's postings, the chosen applicant not only having immense power, but also in the enviable position of being groomed for ambassadorial ranking.

Christopher was watching a waiter rearrange the trays on the table to accommodate a chafing dish when a memory assailed him. He shifted uncomfortably, a frown appearing between the black wings of his eyebrows. *Rachel*—a delicate face, large brown eyes set in dark lashes, hair the colour of honey. *Rachel*. He hadn't thought of her in years or, to be more precise, he'd deliberately put her out of his mind. What was the use in remembering? He'd been young then, beginning his career; she had still been in the middle of college. It had been the sort of affair that only the very young and the very romantic can have. Of course, it hadn't lasted. Why should it? Both of them had had their own lives to lead, ambitions to follow, careers to pursue. He'd been better off out of it. He knew that.

Still, it wasn't easy for Christopher to banish Rachel back into that special compartment in his mind where he, subconsciously, lodged the unfinished business of his psyche. It was like an old attic where furniture was stored, the curves of backs and arms of chairs shrouded by sheets, their outlines blurred and shadowy. Memories were safe there, hidden so that they didn't haunt his conscious moments and open wounds that seemed to have healed. He'd kept Rachel there for years, tucked deep inside, buried beneath the knowledge of other women.

Oh, he'd known that returning to Washington would bring it all back, but he'd thought that the memories could be shrugged off, easily put aside. He hadn't realised that they'd be no less vivid for having been kept under wraps for so long. Rachel's face obliterated the library from his vision; he could remember the softness of her between his hands, the taste of her mouth on his, a long, bare leg sliding out from between tangled . . .

'Damn'! The curse was low and muttered, but it caught the attention of one of the caterers who gave him a curious look as she rearranged a cheese platter. Christopher turned away, walked back through the sliding glass doors that separated the entrance of the Embassy from its offices and nodded to the guard. A lot of water had gone under the bridge since Rachel, he thought as he pressed the button that called down the lift. He was thirty-five now, he'd had other affairs, and he had no reason to even believe that she lived in Washington anymore. The memories would fade with time. He'd get caught up in the Washington of today, and the Washington of ten years ago would wane in comparison.

Perhaps there might be another woman, sitting in the wings of his future, ready to enter—stage left—into the centre of his life. He was tired of casual encounters, indifferent liaisons, the fumbled gropings of one-night stands. He wanted a woman, but she was formless and faceless. The only thing Christopher knew with any certainty was that he'd recognise her immediately. He'd know her by a smile, a tilt of her head, eyes that would look into his soul. He couldn't have articulated this feeling in words—he was neither sentimental nor romantic—but the feeling of expectation remained in him, and he would glance at a woman with a look that was often mistaken by her as sexual attraction. But it wasn't that at all. Christopher was merely searching, curious and hopeful, for the indescribable, for the not yet defined quality that would fill the emptiness of his heart.

'Dr Sims? Mrs Maloney is on the line.'

Rachel looked up from her desk and smiled at Molly's raised, expressive eyebrows. Molly was the receptionist for their paediatric office, a black woman of fifty who'd been nursing for twenty-five years and had had six children of her own. She could diagnose almost any childhood ailment from cradle cap to rubella, and she didn't hesitate to put in her opinion when an opportunity presented itself. It was a private joke among the doctors that, if they all left tomorrow, the patients would never notice. Molly was quite capable of managing all by herself.

'Is it that rash?'

'She's sure it's not a heat rash.' Molly's round face

expressed her disgust over the panicky fears of new mothers.

'She might be right, you know,' Rachel said. She had learned early on in her residency that a mother's ignorance of medicine was often outweighed by an instinctive reaction to her infant that surpassed even a doctor's diagnosis.

Molly didn't look convinced. 'Do you want to talk to her or should she bring him in tomorrow morning?'

Rachel weighed the life and death possibilities of a skin rash in her mind and said, 'First thing tomorrow morning, but tell her to give him a bath with baking soda if he's uncomfortable.'

'Who wouldn't be uncomfortable?' Molly muttered as she left. 'It's so hot out there you could fry eggs on the pavement.'

Rachel smiled, took off her reading glasses and rubbed the skin of her nose in a weary gesture. Her day was running overtime as usual. There'd been an outbreak of chicken pox in the city, hundreds of their patients seemed to need physicals for summer camp and there'd been the usual assortment of ailments that seemed to attack babies in the heat; rashes, upset stomachs, listlessness. It had, she supposed, been an ordinary day in the life of a paediatrician, but she'd been on the go since five o'clock that morning and she was tired.

She wondered if she could call Rob and cancel out on that cocktail party. She didn't know where it was or who it was for; she'd simply accepted because Rob was a sweetheart, and she owed him more than she could ever thank him for. He'd been a mentor, a guide, a fountain of encouragement when medical school had threatened her sanity, and instrumental in getting her a position in an already well-established paediatric practice. When he'd called up last night, she hadn't the heart to tell him that she hated cocktail parties.

'It will be good for you to get out,' Rob had chided her. 'You've been working night and day.'

'There's so much to do,' she had said. 'It's endless.'

'You can be only so conscientious,' he said. 'I've watched plenty of doctors work themselves into an early grave and that didn't do their patients any good.' Dr Robert Mason was a director of research at the National Institute of Health, a good friend of her family and the closest thing to a father that she'd ever had.

'But there might be a crisis or a . . .'

'I'll be waiting outside your office at six-thirty, and I want you to wear that green dress. I like it.'

Rachel had laughed. 'Aye, aye, sir,' she had said crisply.

'That's better,' Rob had growled. 'There's nothing nicer than an obedient woman.'

'Chauvinist,' she had said accusingly.

'Six-thirty or I'll come up there and drag you out myself.'

Rachel stacked up the files on her desk, noted that the Simpson baby would be hospitalised in the morning, and reminded herself to check the blood count for the Brewer boy as soon as she got in to office tomorrow. Then, in a slow and luxurious movement, she stretched her arms over her head, brought them down and pulled the pins out of her hair, rubbing at her scalp where they had left indentations. The honey-blonde curls tumbled around her shoulders, outlining a face with wide brown eyes, a narrow nose, a mouth that was only slightly curved. In repose, Rachel's face held a hint of severity to it, as if she could never quite rid herself of the seriousness of life. When she laughed, her features were transformed. She had a smile that travelled to her eyes, lighting their depths and warming anyone who watched her. Although she was not beautiful in any classical sense of the word, Rachel had 0 liveliness of spirit that made her seem lovely.

She changed into the green dress that Rob had requested. She knew why he liked it; most men did. It

was silk, fitted snugly over her curves and had a back
that almost plunged out of sight. The skirt was straight,
the bodice cut into a V *décolletage*. It was what Rachel
called a man's dress, revealing less than it promised but
hinting at excitement. With it she wore white high-
heeled sandals, a simple gold chain around her neck
and gold hoops at her ears. In it, she was transformed
from Dr Sims, dedicated doctor, to Rachel Sims, single
woman at large.

She washed her face in the bathroom that went with
the office, brushed her teeth, reapplied her make-up and
brushed her hair until it crackled. Then she clipped back
its heavy curls with two gold combs, stared in the
mirror for a second and made a grimace at her own
face. Cocktail parties; she'd been at enough of those to
last her a lifetime. Once, they'd been a part and parcel
of the heady excitement of a love affair. She and
Christopher had gone sometimes to two or three a
week, nibbling away at the food, watching the crowd
and laughing.

How they had laughed—that's what Rachel remembered most, the laughter. The sheer enjoyment of
being with him, the exhilaration of touching him.
Christopher had been her first lover, and she had never
guessed that such sensations could exist or that sex
could be so wonderful until he had shown her that it
was so. She hadn't planned on sleeping with him,
although in the back of her mind she had known . . .
well, admitted secretly to herself, that she wanted to
and would if he asked her. He was so totally different
than the boys she had known whose fumbling advances
had made her shrink from the typical sort of teenage
experimentation.

But they had only gone out three times, and he had
seemed so cool, so composed, that she had wondered if,
perhaps, he wasn't interested. And then they'd spent the
day climbing in the Virginia mountains, a warm autumn
day when the trees above their heads were thick with

russet and orange foliage and the ground was covered in a bed of leaves. They had wandered into an isolated thicket, miles from anyone else, where the only sounds were the chatter of squirrels and the shrill singing of birds. She had run into the thicket, laughing at the sheer joy of being there, of being alive, of being with a man that she found exciting almost beyond endurance. And then she had tripped over a rock and fallen, still laughing, into a crinkly mass of leaves. Christopher had tried to grab her, missed and then fallen himself. For a while, they had both lain there, breathing hard, laughing so hard they couldn't talk. And then he had turned to her, taken her into his arms, and she'd discovered that he hadn't been cool at all. Not at all . . .

Rachel had, in her naïve way, thought it would last forever. There was an exuberance in her nature that had overflowed in Christopher's presence, a cornucopia of happiness and well-being. He, who was sombre by nature, had been charmed and delighted by it. They had fallen in love with a suddenness that had taken both their breaths away, and had shared a passion that seemed boundless. It had seemed to Rachel that she and Christopher existed in a splendid isolation from the rest of the world—floating in an iridescent bubble high above the needs and concerns of ordinary citizens, their sustenance nothing more than passion and love. Her mother had warned her, even Rob had said his piece, but Rachel hadn't listened. Looking back, she understood that there hadn't been anything they could have said that would have made even the slightest dent in the glittering surface of her dreams. Love, that young and innocent love, had made her blind, deaf and dumb.

Of course, it hadn't lasted. Affairs like that rarely do, do they? The reality that they had willingly ignored for so long entered into their lives. The needs of jobs and ambitions had tugged at them; circumstance had torn them apart. Their inability to compromise had caused them to quarrel angrily. They had said bitter things to one another. Home truths that had once laid mercifully below the surface rose to their lips and were spoken. That glittering surface of dreams had broken around Rachel in sharp, pointed shards, their final argument leaving her with the sensation that she'd been pierced, as if Christopher—with those harsh words—had drilled painful holes in her heart.

She had recovered, of course, no one actually died of love, but she had thought, for some time, that she might. Her exuberance had seeped out of her, leaving her tired, drained and exhausted. For months she had done nothing but eat and sleep, reading occasionally and crying a great deal. Her mother had conferred with Rob, the two of them had insisted that she finish her application to medical school. Slowly, Rachel had pulled herself back into the mainstream of existence, getting up in the morning like other people, going to classes, doing her work, participating in conversations and, finally, learning to smile again.

But she had never quite gone back to the Rachel who had been Christopher Blake's lover; that Rachel, light-hearted and free from the knowledge of pain, was gone forever, a snapshot in an old, rarely looked at album. The new Rachel was more serious and less inclined to trust either the men she met or her own judgment about them. She dated still, her love life was adequate for a medical student who almost had no time for the opposite sex, but she allowed no man close to her heart. Christopher had left an indelible impression, a legacy of hurt and pain. She shied away from any relationship that smacked of anything beyond a casual commitment. Rachel had learned, the hard way, just how dangerous it was to fall in love.

She finished dressing, tidied up her office and hung her white coat on its hook behind the door. When she stepped out of the door to the office building, the heat hit her like a palpable force. It was mid-June, and already the Washington summer was underway, a season that combined high temperature with an intense humidity. The city had been originally built on the dampness of a marsh, and nothing its builders had accomplished could change that fact. Rachel lifted the heaviness of her hair off the back of her neck and wished that she'd worn it up. She could already feel small beads of perspiration forming on her upper lip.

'You look wonderful!' Rob came up the steps to where she was standing and, lifting her hand, forced her to pirouette in a small circle. 'Love that dress. Whenever you wear it, I wish I were thirty years younger.'

Rachel smiled and kissed him on his shaved and cologned cheek. 'Gallantry becomes you,' she said, thinking how distinguished he looked with his thick salt-and-pepper hair and clear blue eyes. Rob wasn't much taller than she was, but what he lacked in height he made up for in pizzazz. He was a snappy dresser, and she was amused to see that the faint red pinstripe in his blue suit was picked up in the red of his tie. Rob was a man of sixty who was still trim, still athletic and, since he was very much a bachelor, decidedly still flirtatious whenever he got the chance.

'That's all that's left to an old man,' Rob said morosely as they walked towards his car.

'Old man? What do you mean by that?'

'When a fellow of my age goes out with a young lady of yours, he'd better be gallant. Otherwise he's called some very uncomplimentary names.'

'Really, Rob, aren't you being a bit morbid? Sixty is hardly old.'

'I'm feeling my years, sweetheart.' Rob opened the door on her side. 'Aches and pains, an arthritic knee. I can't jog the way I used to.'

'Ten miles a day down to two?' Rachel asked as she sat down in the front seat.

'Not much sympathy here,' he said gruffly, addressing

the sky as if looking for aid. 'I don't know why I try.' And then he closed her door before she could answer.

Rachel smiled to herself as Rob walked around the front of the car and to his own door. When she'd been five, Rob had taken her to the park, pushed the swing for her and patiently spent hours helping her build cakes in the sandbox. When she had been thirteen, awkward and gangly, Rob had invited her out to dinner at one of Washington's poshest restaurants and had treated her as if she were the most glamorous woman there. Now that she was thirty, he had established with her a jocular repartee that was two parts avuncular and one part flirtatious, a combination that satisfied his vision of himself as both her protector and ladies' man.

'So how are the children of Washington?' Rob asked as he sat down, closed his door and put the key in the ignition.

'Full of chicken pox.'

'Itchy little devils.'

'With nappy rashes or colic or sun burn.'

'I told you to go into surgery, but you insisted on babies.'

Rachel smoothed down her skirt as Rob pulled away from the kerb. The air-conditioning in his car blew cool air across her knees and down to her ankles. 'I enjoy treating children and, besides, I would have been a rotten surgeon. I hate inflicting pain.'

'I had dreams of you as a surgeon.'

'I know,' she said. It was Rob who had put the dreams of medicine into her head, his stories of doctoring merging in with the plots of certain television shows until Rachel had seen herself as another saviour of the human race. Dr Rachel Sims, emergency doctor, crusading physician, surgeon. Even when she'd been old enough to know the reality—the energy required, the hard work, the long hours—the dream had still remained.

'And how's Phyllis?'

Rachel threw Rob a quick glance, but he had his eyes on the heavy traffic on Massachusetts Avenue. Lately, Rob had been enquiring after her mother with an unusual frequency. The questions had brought back to Rachel certain childhood fantasies. For years, she had wanted Rob to be her father. When she was very small, this wish had not included marriage to her mother; she'd been too young to understand the real connections between parents. But as she got older, she had dreamed of Phyllis marrying Rob, of a real church wedding, of being a flower girl in a long, white, lacy dress with pink flowers in her hair.

This fantasy had held a tight grasp on her imagination right up until the time she was fifteen and wondered if, maybe, just perhaps, *she* might marry Rob. Of course, he was a little old for her, but then again, it was more than likely, wasn't it, that Rob had been waiting for her to grow up? Rachel had nursed this delusion along, thinking about it in both an idle and curious way, until the day she'd caught sight of Rob and another woman in one of the art museums, walking together and holding hands. When she'd asked her mother about it, Phyllis had said in a dry sort of way, 'A blonde? I guess he's replaced the redhead with a newer model.' It was then that Rachel had understood that their Rob, the friend and quasi-uncle, was not the marrying type.

But then Phyllis had sold the house, pulled up her roots and moved to North Carolina. She'd been waiting, she said, for Rachel to finish school, a time when she would be free of responsibilities and comfortable in the knowledge that Rachel could now support herself. She had always dreamed of living by the ocean and had bought a small cottage among the dunes that overlooked the Atlantic. Ever since her departure Rob had been enquiring after her. It made Rachel wonder if he missed Phyllis's company after all those years.

'She's fine. Painting up a storm. She says she loves the beach and the dunes. The light's always changing.'

His voice was non-committal. 'She sounds happy.'

'You know my mother. She's the type to make herself happy anywhere.'

Rob deftly pulled around a car stalled at an intersection, two buses and a blaring taxi. 'I suppose she's made some friends?'

Rachel thought to herself—now, isn't that a leading question?—but all she said was, 'I imagine so.'

'Is she planning any visits back?'

Rachel shook her head. 'She has announced the following: that she won't return to Washington except to visit her grandchildren.'

This time it was Rob who gave her a quick look. 'Any chance of that?'

Rachel laughed. 'Not without a husband.'

'What about the last fellow that was hanging around? The radiologist.'

'Ugh.'

Rob raised his eyebrows as the car swept around Dupont Circle. 'He seemed nice enough to me.'

'*You* didn't have to go out with him.'

'Now, listen to me, my dear. You're living a very sterile existence, weighing babies and looking at sore throats.'

Rachel threw her hands up in mock horror. 'Rob! Surely, *you're* not advocating marriage, are you?'

'Nothing drastic, sweetheart. But you need to have some fun. You're not old enough to bury yourself behind a prescription pad.'

Rachel had found it increasingly difficult to explain to both her mother and Rob just how content she really was. Medical school had been a long, expensive and difficult grind followed by two years of interning and a three-year residency in paediatrics. By the time she had received her medical degree, Rachel had known just what she wanted to be, and the hours she spent in her office seeing children were some of the happiest of her life. Although she wasn't celibate—there had been a couple of lovers in the past ten years—she didn't feel any compelling urge to find a man to complete her life. She was far from lonely, her work involved most of her mental and physical energies and she derived a great deal of satisfaction from finally being independent and self-supporting. Nothing gave her more pleasure than opening the door to her own apartment in the evening, the one that she could now afford and furnish just the way she wanted.

'There are many definitions of "fun",' she began and then happened to notice where they were as Rob slowed the car down and pulled it next to the kerb.

'And you're missing most of them,' Rob replied.

But Rachel wasn't capable of responding to Rob's affectionate goading. A totally irrational and unforeseen surge of emotion rushed through her. Her heart had begun to clamour wildly in her chest, a lump of fear formed in her throat, and her hands had clenched into fists on her lap.

Rob, however, was far too taken up with parking to notice Rachel's sudden panic. 'That was lucky,' he added. 'A spot right in front.'

But Rachel barely noticed how fortunate they were. She was staring at the building; the curved driveway, the ornate stone façade, the wrought iron double door, the red-and-white flag hanging over the portico.

'What are we doing here?' she asked, her voice breathless.

'Didn't I tell you?' Rob leaned over and turned off the ignition. 'The cocktail party is at the Canadian Embassy. We're celebrating a joint agreement to fund cancer research.'

The memories were flooding back, images of entering that building, pulling open the heavy doors, walking down the burgundy carpet to the guard who sat behind the bullet-proof sliding glass door. 'Christopher Blake.'

she would say to him through the speaking hole. 'Oh, yes, Miss Sims,' the guard would reply. All the guards had come to know who she was, but they always went through the ritual of security; calling Christopher's office, checking to see that her presence was legitimate before pushing the button that let the doors automatically open and allowing her to walk into the part of the building that was off limits to anyone who was not classified personnel. Rachel had read recently that the Canadian government had bought a tract of land on Pennsylvania Avenue and intended to build another Embassy, but for her, it would always be here, in a building that had once been a private residence with high ceilings, carved wood-panelled walls and a sweeping staircase that led to the second floor.

Rob was still talking about the agreement, his voice filled with satisfaction. 'It'll be a great opportunity,' he was saying, 'for a pooling of information and resources, a scholarly exchange . . .'

What was wrong with her? She had passed by the Embassy hundreds of times since Christopher had left and had scarcely given it a moment's notice. Now, the thought of entering it had set off a maelstrom of memories and emotions that were totally inappropriate for the occasion. Christopher wasn't in there; in fact, all the faces she had known would be gone. That's the way a foreign service worked. The working force was rotational; people came and went, their postings lasting only a few years. Christopher had left Washington to go to Paris. She hadn't any idea where he'd gone since then; they had never contacted one another after that last final argument. He could be anywhere—Nairobi, Chile—Denmark, but the chances of him being back in Washington were so remote that they were hardly worth contemplating. A Washington posting at whatever level was a sought-after position, and Rachel knew that the Canadian government rarely granted one twice.

Still, Rachel was far tenser than she liked. Her spine was rigid to the cushion behind her, and she could feel the strain of stress in her neck. Very deliberately she unclenched her hands, forcing them to lie in her lap in gentle curves. Then she turned to Rob and tried to concentrate on what he was saying, hoping that the words would pour over her like a soothing balm.

'. . . and, of course, NIH will be involved with the Canadian Medical Research Council and they've done some good work on the new drugs.'

'That's great,' Rachel said.

'So let's go, shall we?'

She gave Rob a smile. 'After you.'

He got out of the car, walked around her side and opened her door. 'God, it's hot,' she said as she stepped out of the air-conditioning and back into the early evening heat. Even at this time of day, the temperature was in the mid-90s, the pavement hot to the touch and radiating warmth upwards.

Rob patted her hand as she slipped her arm into the crook of his elbow. 'You look as cool as a cucumber.'

'Do I?'

'And lovely,' he said as they began to walk up the curved drive.

'Flatterer.'

'Nonsense, I'm not so blind that I don't know when I've got a beautiful woman on my . . .' Rob stopped for a moment and looked down at her, a sudden frown in his blue eyes. 'Of course, I forgot. You've been here before.'

She gave him a reassuring smile, knowing that what Rob was remembering was the painful aftermath of her affair with Christopher; the tears, the exhaustion, the depression. 'It was a long time ago.'

'And what was his name again?'

'Christopher Blake.'

'Oh, yes.' Rob squinted his eyes as if he were trying to picture Christopher Blake in his mind and then he

shrugged. 'Well, it's all water under the bridge, isn't it?'
he asked hopefully.

'Yes,' Rachel said very firmly. 'It certainly is.'

Christopher was late getting to the cocktail party. He
was caught in his office doing something he found to be
one of the most distasteful aspects of his job—dealing
with an unpleasant personnel problem. As Minister,
Christopher could wheel and deal in some of the
world's highest political arenas, and he thoroughly
enjoyed the cut and thrust of negotiation, but the
managerial aspects of being second to the top at the
Embassy also put him in the position of handling
unhappy subordinates. And it was the truly difficult
and thorny problems that made it up to his level.
Unconsciously, he sighed as his political attaché, Tom
Ferguson, laid the issue of Mary and Frank Newman
before him.

'The man shouldn't have been posted here,' Tom was
saying. 'He was taken out of Agriculture and sent here
as assistant to Braker, but he's in trouble. And it's
obvious that his wife's miserable. She's sick half the
time, his kids are a problem, and he can't seem to
handle the responsibilities of . . .'

Ferguson droned on and on, itemising Frank
Newman's offending behaviour and listing Mary
Newman's failures as an Embassy wife. Christopher
had heard it so many times before that he thought he
could have recited the litany in his dreams.

Foreign service marriages had a way of either coming
apart at the seams under the stress of postings or
pulling together to make a strong and durable family
unit. Assignments in poor and backward countries were
the hardest; even European posts could be difficult.
Many people assumed that Washington would be easy
for Canadians because it was English-speaking and had
a North American culture, but the situation was more
complicated than that. Washington wasn't like Ottawa;

it was big, crime-ridden, complex and high-pressured. Mary wasn't the first wife to crack in it or Frank the first employee not to do well at the Embassy. Christopher had heard of others.

Everyone was sympathetic; even Ferguson, cynical bastard that he was, looked unhappy. Frank was a nice guy; Mary was sweet. The trouble was that he was the wrong man in the wrong job at the wrong time and getting rid of him not only involved giving the man a poor job rating, but also the tremendous expense of moving the Newmans, lock, stock and barrel, back to Ottawa and replacing them with someone else.

'Okay,' Christopher said. 'Let me get this straight. He's been here eight months without a sign of improvement or adjustment. Is the problem Newman or his wife?'

Ferguson shrugged. 'It's hard to tell where one leaves off and the other begins. Frank's no genius, but I suppose he might have done better if he didn't have all these problems at home.'

'And his wife wants out?'

'That's what she tells everyone. Cynthia spent an hour talking to her on the 'phone over the weekend.' Cynthia was Tom's wife, a model Embassy spouse, who had the poise, style and grace to carry off what was demanded of her. She was part of the reason Tom was where he was. A contented Embassy wife was an invaluable asset; an unhappy one usually meant that a man's career as a foreign service officer would be terminated almost before it began.

'I assume they have a diplomatic clause in their lease.'

'The Embassy doesn't approve the leases unless it's included.'

'Eight months,' Christopher said musingly and Tom caught the message.

'We could give him another six—although Braker will go nuts if he doesn't straighten up.'

Christopher shook his head. 'It would be easier to move them now at the beginning of the summer. That way their kids won't be caught in the middle of a school year.' There was no simple hiring and firing at a post. Moves involved families and family rhythms. For a bachelor, Christopher was surprisingly sensitive to the needs of children; it was one of the oddities of his personality that impressed the women he went out with. Other than that, none of them had been able to see him in the role of a domesticated man.

'Yeah, that's true,' Tom conceded.

'How will he take it?'

'Frank? Badly—he doesn't want to admit he's not doing well.'

Christopher sighed, picked up a pencil and twirled it in his fingers. It was now up to him to decide whether to sit on it or make his decision which he would pass along to the Ambassador. Christopher didn't have the actual power to send Frank Newman back to Ottawa, but his appraisal of the situation would be crucial.

'I'll want to talk to Braker,' he finally said, knowing that Tom wouldn't like the implication that he hadn't assessed the problem well enough. But forcing the Newmans back to Ottawa would be traumatic for them, and Christopher had to be certain he was doing the right thing.

If Tom didn't like Christopher's words, he didn't show it. The eyes behind his tortoise-rimmed glasses were carefully non-committal. 'Fine.'

'And I'd like some sort of informal situation in which I can meet the Newmans and see what they're like.'

This time, Tom inadvertently gave away his surprise. His mouth dropped open.

Christopher leaned forward and gave Tom a cold look out of his grey eyes. 'It's brutal,' he said, 'to fire a man without giving him a hearing at least.'

'Of course,' Tom said quickly and, standing up, said a few stilted words before leaving.

Christopher swivelled his chair and looked out of his window. It had a view of Massachusetts Avenue and he idly watched the traffic for a few minutes, letting his mind go into neutral before he drummed up the energy to go down the stairs and put on his diplomatic façade for the cocktail party guests. He'd put in long hours since moving to Washington only two weeks before. Trade negotiations between Canada and the US were heating up with hints of tariff restrictions being thrown right, left and centre. Then the Minister was expected to attend numerous high-level dinners and parties, sometimes on his own, sometimes on behalf of the Ambassador who was deluged with invitations. Almost from his day of arrival, Christopher had been rising at five in the morning, jogging before breakfast at seven, putting in a full day's work and then attending some function until nine or ten. He was utterly thankful for one of the best of the Ministerial perks, an Embassy-owned and furnished house that came with an outdoor pool and its own staff. He'd been saved hours of shopping for furniture and trying to find help.

He'd come a long way, Christopher reflected. The Embassy was a lifetime's distance away from being a poor boy from a small prairie town with a railroad running through it and a grain elevator at one end. He had lived there with his mother and, only sporadically, his father in a cramped little house near the railroad tracks. Its wooden siding had been barely protected by peeling grey paint, and its doors hung on crazy angles on the hinges. The window of his room had faced the tracks and the reverberation of the trains coming through town would shake the walls until the mirror rattled over his chest of drawers and his clothes thudded against the door of his wardrobe.

For hours during his childhood, Christopher had sat on his bed and stared at the far horizon, but there had been nothing to see beyond his town except miles of flat, dusty earth, punctuated by the growth of hardy prairie grasses. In the summer the sun burned a golden hole in the blue of the sky; in the winter, it was a pale yellow disc whose meagre warmth was cut to shreds by the fierce cold. His sleep had been puctuated by the whistle of the trains and the shriek of the prairie wind. Sometimes he had dreamt that he was on one of the trains, rushing out of town, down the narrowing track, until he was only a small speck on the brown horizon.

Yes, Christopher thought with an unexpected fierceness, he'd done all right, and there wasn't anyone or anything that could alter the fact that he'd dragged himself up by the boot-straps to one of the most coveted positions in External Affairs. And the future held immense promise—ambassadorial postings that would start in Third World countries and eventually bring him to such glamorous cities as Rome, London, or Paris.

Thoughts of the Newmans drifted into his mind, and he felt the faint toll of a warning bell he'd heard many times before. The lesson was there to be learned by anyone with ambitions in the foreign service. The wrong woman, the wrong marriage, could ruin him. And Christopher, who looked ahead to being an ambassador, was well aware of how much responsibility and stress fell on the wife of a head of post. She had to have a certain kind of strength as well as the attributes of style, sophistication and grace. He hadn't met any woman yet who could fill that position. Not one who could . . .

He suddenly leaned forward and looked intently out of the window. A car had pulled up and a woman was being helped out of the passenger seat by an older man. Christopher couldn't see her face, a cascade of honey-coloured hair shielded that from his view, but he could see the shape of her, and certain details caught his eye. She was of medium-height, slender but curvaceous with long, shapely legs. A watch encircled a narrow wrist. Gold combs glinted in her hair. Then she and her companion slipped out of his view as they walked towards the Embassy doors.

Christopher stared at the grey monolith of the Brookings Institute across the street and then shook his head as if he were shaking off a persistent and irritating fly. For a second, he had thought ... he had actually imagined ... what a ridiculous idea! Imagining that the woman was Rachel because of the colour of her hair and the shape of her body. He'd seen a dozen women in the past ten years who were that size and had blonde hair, and none of them had set off these painful echoes. Why he should now ... *Wishful thinking*? a small voice within him asked, and Christopher ruthlessly squashed it. Nonsense. He'd thought about Rachel earlier. It was simply a sort of ... hangover effect. It didn't mean anything.

He stood up, straightened his tie and buttoned his jacket. Another diplomatic evening, another cocktail party. Perhaps he'd be lucky and have the opportunity to slip away early. He wanted to jog an extra mile or two the next morning; he could use the extra exercise. He'd go deeper into Rockcliffe Park, early in the morning before the day's heat had penetrated through the leaves of the trees. He'd smell the scents of earth, and hear the rustle of small animals in the bush. The steady drumming of his feet, his own panting breath, the rhythm of legs and arms would wipe out old memories and cleanse his imagination. And, when he was finished, his body limp from exhaustion, his mind emptied of anything but the sensation of his heart and muscles, he would be renewed, and that image of Rachel, honey-blonde, seductive and dangerous, would be gone.

CHAPTER TWO

WASHINGTON cocktail parties are unique, not for their food or the procedure which is standard around the world, but for the feeling that one gets from being so close to so much power, wealth and status. Rachel had quite forgotten the aura that hovered over a mixing of people in Washington. Deals were made at parties like this, contacts were established, information passed hands. The importance of such things would have been minimal in some other countries, but not in Washington. When the United States shifted, the rest of the world was shoved to one side. This knowledge gave Washington cocktail parties a larger-than-life aspect, and the party-goers had the sensation that they were movers and shakers on a vast scale. As Rachel entered the room, she could feel the undercurrents. There was an intense discussion being carried out in one corner of the room, a look of satisfaction on a face, anxiety marking another. She knew that the agreement reached between the US and Canada on cancer research was valued in billions of dollars. The politicians had agreed on the basic principle, and it was now up to lesser mortals in the bureaucracies to allocate the funds. The projects of some researchers would be judged as worthless; others as valuable. There were people here, she knew, who were lobbying hard and fast for their own particular bailiwicks.

Then, as she was pulled by Rob into the crowd, Rachel lost that impartiality of an outside observer. She was suddenly in the midst of the cocktail party; the chatter, the clinking of glasses, the shifting of groups around the bar and the long table that held the food. Since the party was being funded by several medical institutions as well as the Embassy, no expense had been spared where food was concerned. There was a three-tiered circular dish that held shrimps on the top level, oysters on the second and chunks of lobster on the bottom, each type of shellfish resting on a bed of glistening ice. There was British Columbia smoked salmon, marinated mushrooms, platters of roast beef and wedges of cheese. Waiters in black circulated throughout the room, carrying silver trays that held canapés or goblets of white wine. It brought the past back to Rachel in a nostalgic way, and she smiled a bit sadly to herself as she sipped at a gin and tonic.

'Have you met Harvey?' Rob was saying.

'No,' Rachel said. 'I haven't.'

The man who had come up to them was not much taller than Rachel, had dark, curly hair and a matching moustache and gave the overall impression of being round. His face was moon-shaped, his tortoise-shell glasses were circular, and, despite the carefully tailored cut of his blue suit, it was apparent that his paunch somewhat approximated that of a basketball. None of this stopped him apparently from thinking that he was God's gift to woman. He gave Rachel a happy leer, eyeing her up and down in an exaggerated way.

'Well . . .' he said gleefully and then, 'Rob, you old son-of-a-gun. You never told me.'

'Told you what?'

'About this fabulous treasure, this magnificent specimen.'

Rob winked at Rachel. 'Are you referring to my date?'

'Date! I'm devastated. Darling, assure me that you have better taste. Surely, you must realise that you're wasted on this man.'

Rachel blinked. 'I . . .'

'Beautiful,' Harvey murmured and then, leaning forward, examined Rachel's décolletage with such scrutiny that she gave Rob an amazed look. He merely grinned at her; it was clear that he and Harvey were old pals. 'Fabulous circulation,' Harvey added with hushed admiration. 'Great haemoglobin.'

'He's in blood research,' Rob said to Rachel by way of an explanation.

Rachel had regained her poise. 'How nice,' she said drily. 'If he gets any closer, I'm going to give him a contusion on his nasal ligaments that will give him a chance to study his own platelets.'

Harvey gave her a delighted smile. 'A sense of humour,' he said. 'A paragon. Rob, who is this lovely?'

'Harvey, Dr Rachel Sims. Rachel, Dr Harvey Campbell.'

'A doctor,' Harvey said in amazement and then, taking Rachel's hand, lifted it to his lips. 'Darling, I'm looking for a doctor.'

Rachel smiled; she couldn't help it. What Harvey lacked in physical presence, he certainly made up for with the sheer effrontery of his flirtation.

'I'm not sure you qualify for my practice,' she said, recovering her hand from his grasp'

'And what's that, darling? Cardiologist? I have a bad heart. Dermatologist? I suffer from a mysterious rash in the most . . . er, unusual places. Chiropodist? I have a foot fetish. Whatever it is, Dr Sims, I'm sure I can find an ailment.' Harvey paused and then looked panicky. 'Unless you're a gynaecologist! No, the gods in heaven wouldn't do that to me. May the celestial sphere look down upon me and smile in pleasure. Rachel, darling, tell me you're in sex therapy.'

'Paediatrics,' she said.

Harvey groaned. 'Peds,' he said with disgust. 'I should have known. How did you end up in that?'

'I . . .'

'I know—you like children.' Harvey went on, supplying the very words that Rachel had been about to say. 'Rob, couldn't you have steered her into something more glamorous like—blood research?'

They all laughed at that. Nothing was less glamorous and more like slugging than the type of work that Harvey spent his days doing—analysing hundreds of blood samples, calculating complex chemical reactions, searching for that small and subtle clue that would lead him to the cause of a disease.

'I tried,' Rob said, 'but she wouldn't have any of it. Actually I wanted her to go into surgery. I . . .'

But Rachel suddenly lost track of what Rob was saying. She'd been laughing and had raised her head, her eyes idling traversing the room. It was then that she'd caught sight of a figure in the doorway and felt the laughter drain right out of her as if a hole had appeared just beneath her feet, a dark vortex that sucked everything into it.

The voices of the guests disappeared, the sounds of glassware, the slight hum of the air-conditioning, Rob's chuckle. Sound was deadened, and the only thing she could actually hear was the beat of her own heart, a heavy and awkward drumming that reverberated through her so that she could feel it in her wrists, her throat, her temples. And her vision was affected. The people around her went out of focus, their faces turning into pale blanks, the colours of their clothes merging into the background. Only the man at the door was clear. She could see every detail as if he had been magnified—just for her.

He stood in three-quarters profile to her, and his face was just as it had been ten years ago except for the addition of wrinkles around his eyes and two strong lines that had been etched from nose to mouth. It was a face that had always seemed beautiful to her in repose; angular and yet pleasing in its masculine planes. The grey eyes were deep-set beneath dark brows, the nose was straight and slightly flared at the base. He had a narrow top lip with a deep indentation beneath the nose and a bottom lip that was fuller and more sensual. His chin was square; his beard always dark beneath the skin no matter how recently he had shaved. The hair that waved over his ears was still black as night but now it was tinted with silver. He looked older than his thirty-five years, and tired as if the ten years had placed heavy burdens on him.

Rachel noticed that he had a shaving nick on his neck just above the white of his collar. And, as he raised his hand to smooth back his hair, she caught a glimpse of a silver digital watch. She wondered what he had done with the one she had so carefully chosen for him. That one had been gold but not digital. She could remember the sound of it ticking in her ear at night when his arm lay across her.

His fingers were the ones that had touched her once; long and unadorned. He wore no rings, but then Rachel knew that Christopher didn't like rings. It was an idiosyncrasy of his: he didn't think that men should wear rings. Of course, that didn't mean anything. The fact that his fingers were bare of rings. The fact that he wore no wedding band. He could have married; he could have a family for all she . . . His hand dropped then, and he smiled as someone walked past him. The smile smoothed the hard angles, curved the lips upward and deepened the wrinkles at his eyes. Rachel forgot everything but that smile. It wasn't one that she remembered; there was a wariness to it, a reserve held behind it. It wasn't quite real, and the thought came quickly to her—*he isn't happy*. Then she thrust it away. Ten years of absence was a long time. Too long, really, to know another person still. He was a stranger, that's all. A dark stranger in a doorway.

But then his head turned so that he saw her. She saw the shock of recognition widen his eyes, the grimace of pain pass over his face before he got the muscles back into control again. And then she knew what she had not known before—that she had hurt him as much as he had hurt her. A grim triumph flared within her, an unexpected exultation at the knowledge of his pain, and she was shocked at herself. Rachel hadn't known that so much anger remained within her; she'd thought that she had successfully exorcised the emotional ghosts of her past years ago. Quickly, she moved her head so that she was no longer looking at him, but she could still feel that grey gaze on her, burning as it touched her skin.

'Rachel? Were you listening?'

'Sorry, Rob. What were you saying?'

'Would you like another gin and tonic? Your glass is empty.'

Rachel lifted up her glass and blinked at it. 'Oh—yes, I suppose so.'

'And what about you, Harvey? You're not drinking.'

'I'm dieting,' Harvey said sadly, 'but a Perrier with lime would be fine.'

Rob disappeared into the crowd, and Rachel tried hard to concentrate on the man at her side.

'Your research . . .' she began but Harvey waved a plump hand nonchalantly in the air.

'Boring,' he announced. 'I'd rather hear about you. Tell me about your practice.'

'Well,' Rachel said, 'I'm one of four doctors. Thomas is a paediatric allergist . . .'

'A great field,' Harvey said. 'Washington must have more allergic children per square inch than in any other part of the country.'

Rachel nodded her head in agreement, trying hard to smile and not to think of the tall figure who must be circulating through the room. 'It's such a damp climate. Too much mould.'

'And who else is there?'

'Brian—a paediatric surgeon. He's at the hospital most of the time, but he takes all our patients who need surgery. He had an interesting case last week, a child with intestinal blockage that turned out to . . .' Rachel could hear herself babbling, but she couldn't seem to stop the uncontrollable urge to keep talking. It was as if the words could form a shield around her, protecting her from Christopher's presence. Every nerve ending that she owned was aware of him, and each one responded in its own physiological fashion. Her cheeks burned, the back of her neck was icy, her hands were trembling so hard that she'd clenched them into fists at her side. She didn't dare look around to see where *he* was so she focused on Harvey's spectacled face, and he was beaming with pleasure. It was clear that he thought he had made a conquest.

'Rachel, my sweet, we must get together for lunch sometime. You do get away from those bawling infants for lunch, don't you?'

'I ...' She was going to refuse him. Rachel didn't want to lead Harvey on; she wasn't the least bit interested in him as either a sexual or romantic partner. She wouldn't have minded a friendship; he was funny and witty, but Rachel knew enough about men to recognise Harvey's type. A luncheon together would be taken as a sign of interest; a smile, even mildly flirtatious, would be read as encouragement. Harvey was the kind of guy whose enthusiasm for women was so overwhelming, he was blind to anything but his own urges. Rachel cleared her throat and started again, 'I really don't ...'

'Rachel.' The voice was deep and unmistakable. 'What a surprise.'

His hand was outstretched, and Rachel was forced to take it. She felt the warmth of his palm against hers and, as he moved his hand away, his fingers sliding against her skin, a distinct shiver ran down her spine. That shocked her even more than her earlier feeling of triumph. Rachel had thought, truly thought, that the strong physical attraction she had once felt for Christopher was dead. She had not thought about him in that way for years. The backs of tall, dark men had long since stopped having the power to make her feel that jolt of physical recognition. The sight of a couple kissing no longer brought back the embraces of ten years before. But now it seemed that the years were erased, wiped out with the touch of one hand against hers. Desire had entered her veins and her arteries, circulating through her, causing her pulse to race slightly and a warmth to uncurl deep within.

'Yes,' she said, her voice careful and precise. 'A surprise.'

Christopher turned to Harvey. 'Sorry, but I don't think we've met. I'm Christopher Blake. I'm with the Embassy.'

Harvey was pumping his hand enthusiastically. 'Harvey Campbell. NIH, blood research.'

'It was good of you to come tonight.'

Harvey shrugged. 'It's a great agreement. The combined research should bring a lot of results.'

Christopher shifted his attention back to Rachel. 'And you're with NIH, too?'

Rachel had regained her poise. 'No,' she said coolly, 'I'm in private practice.'

One dark eyebrow curved upwards. 'Really?'

'Paediatrics.'

Only the smallest flicker in his eyes demonstrated Christopher's acknowledgment of her success. Ten years ago, Rachel had been in pre-med and dreaming about being a doctor. 'Congratulations,' he said.

'And you?' she asked. 'I don't suppose you're First Secretary anymore.' He'd been so ambitious, Rachel remembered that. He had never once looked behind him, down the ladder to all the positions that led up to his. Instead, Christopher had set his sights on those places farther up the rungs, to the dizzying heights of ambassadorial postings and high commissioners.

'Minister.'

She acknowledged his success with a nod. 'Congratulations.'

'And your mother . . . Phyllis. How is she?'

'Fine. I'll let her know you were asking after her.'

'I always liked Phyllis.'

'Yes, I remember. And your mother . . .?'

If the words were hard to say, Christopher's expression didn't show it. 'She died. Two years ago.'

'Oh! I'm sorry.' That must have been hard for him, Rachel thought. He'd been very close to his mother.

Harvey had followed this terse conversation with a small frown. It was clear that he was getting the odd vibrations and didn't know what to make of them. 'So you two knew one another before?'

'I was in Washington ten years ago. Rachel and I . . . are old friends.'

Old friends—what an ambiguous, evasive term that was. It could cover anything from a chance acquaintance to a lovers' intimacy; it evoked emotions from casual affection to intense passion. Old friends. It implied one of those relationships that two people could take on and off with ease—like a pair of old shoes or a well-worn sweater. It did not cover the way Rachel felt with Christopher standing so close to her that she could smell the faint lime odour of his cologne. What she felt was uncomfortable and confused, knowing that she wanted him again and still angry from battles she had fought years ago. And she'd quite forgotten how tall he was or wide his shoulders were. She'd forgotten what it felt like to stand next to him, knowing that if she leaned against him, her cheek would rest against the upper part of his arm, the tweedy texture of his suit rubbing against her skin.

'Old friends,' Harvey repeated, staring from one to the other. 'Hey, that's great.'

'Yes, it is, isn't it, Rachel?'

Rachel didn't think it was great at all, and she knew Christopher didn't either. Not that you could tell anything from his face. It was a smooth mask, hiding his emotions from view. Even the grey eyes were shuttered so that she couldn't tell if he were laughing at her or not. She wondered how and where Christopher had acquired such a hard polish, remembering that the man she had known ten years ago had been open and far easier to read. Christopher at twenty-five had still been boyish in ways. He'd had a curiosity about the world, a desire to please and an endearing shyness. None of that remained. Rachel didn't know what experience had turned Christopher into the man who now stood before her, but she would bet that they had not been pleasant. He was aloof and reserved; there was an air to him that suggested a jaded boredom with life.

'It's wonderful to see you again,' she said drily.

'Perhaps we should get together.'

Was he mocking her? There was no way to tell; his eyes were enigmatic as they rested on her face. 'Perhaps,' she said in her vaguest tone.

'Talk about old times.'

Yes, he had to be mocking her. What was there to say about old times that they had not already said a million times with a vicious bitterness? Suddenly, Rachel was angry, but she couldn't show it, not in this room of well-dressed people, all chatting together so aimably, so politely. 'Some time,' she murmured.

'Some time,' Christopher agreed and there was only a hint of dryness to his tone. Then he nodded to Harvey. 'It was nice meeting you.'

He was gone then, moving on to the next group of people, acting out his part as diplomat. Rachel stared at his back, at the fine cut of his jacket, the white rim of his collar, the neat and precise way his black hair was cut at the neck. It had suddenly occurred to her that Christopher might have meant what he said; he might try to see her again. Her mouth went dry at the thought of it.

'So—as I was saying,' Harvey continued, 'about lunch.'

Rachel turned back and gave him the full benefit of one of her loveliest smiles. She wasn't quite aware of what she was doing; she only knew that she had to forget about the man who stood only two feet away from her, his dark head bending to hear another conversation. 'Yes?' she said.

Harvey was practically preening himself over that smile. 'Shall we meet next week then?'

Harvey's question barely slid into her consciousness. Surely, Christopher must understand, Rachel was thinking. He couldn't possibly be serious; he must have been having a small joke at her expense. Too much water had passed under the bridge; too many harsh words had been spoken. Or else, had he thought ... God, no ... he couldn't. He couldn't possibly think that she'd go to bed with him again. Not just like that. Not even if he wined her and dined her, wooing her with all the old charm. She'd have to be crazy to throw herself back into the same old situation again. She'd have to be a madwoman!

Rachel suddenly became aware that Harvey was looking at her with anticipation, his brown eyes blinking at her behind the circles of his glasses. What had he wanted? she wondered.

A woman behind her laughed and said, 'Christopher! Shame on you.'

Rachel's head ached, her thoughts spinning through her mind like whirling dervishes, alighting down for a brief second and then lifting off again, leaving her with half-formed ideas, broken images, semi-speculations. Their affair was over, wasn't it? she thought wildly. And nothing had changed. Nothing.

'Rachel?'

She focused on Harvey's round, eager face. 'Sure,' she said, not knowing or caring what she was agreeing to.

'Terrific,' Harvey said. 'I know a great French place downtown. The sauce béchamel will make your heart swoon.' And he kissed the tips of his fingers in the Gallic fashion, his face beaming with satisfaction.

Which was how Rachel ended up accepting a date with Harvey Campbell.

*   *   *

'What do you mean—you want me to come along?' Samantha Foley stood before a mirror in Bloomingdale's and stared at the suit that now adorned her petite frame.

'I need some protection.'

Samantha turned around and twisted her head so that she could see her own back. 'What do you think?'

Rachel sighed and leaned against the dressing-room wall. 'I think Harvey Campbell is one of those types who will take a yard and a half when you're only offering a quarter of an inch.'

'Rachel! I'm talking about the suit.'

'It's nice,' Rachel said absent-mindedly. 'It looks great on you.'

'You're letting me down,' Samantha said, twisting her shoulders slightly and surveying the cut of the back. 'Your mind is miles away.'

'I'll bring it back if you promise to come with me.'

Samantha turned around and surveyed Rachel. 'You're serious.'

'I've never been more serious in my life.'

'You want me to go out on a date with you? Rachel, honey, you're over twenty-one and smart enough to take care of yourself. What gives?'

Rachel smiled at the picture Samantha made, standing with her legs spread belligerently apart and her hands on her hips, elbows akimbo. It was exactly the sort of pose that Samantha took when her five-year-old daughter, Ellie, acted up, spoke out of turn or was behaving in a particularly obnoxious way. Samantha's head was tilted to one side, her brown eyebrows were drawn together in a frown, and her nose, small and freckled, had a wrinkle in it. Samantha wasn't pretty in any traditional sense, but she had a vivacity that was very attractive and a figure that, for her size, was perfect.

'What gives is that this guy loves women—excessively.'

Samantha turned back towards the mirror. 'Consider

yourself lucky. Think of the number of men that don't like women at all.'

'Sam—I really need your help.'

'The suit first.'

'Buy it.'

'You really do know how to twist a girl's arm, don't you?'

'This is the tenth suit you've tried on,' Rachel said warningly.

Samantha sighed, appraised her trim figure in the blue linen and then nodded. 'I suppose you're right. All right, I'll take it. I'm not crazy about it, but I really need a suit for the office. My dark blue one has had it and . . .'

'And what about Harvey?'

'It doesn't seem right, Rachel. After all . . .'

Rachel grinned and brought out her ammunition. 'Remember William Schaffer.'

Samantha gave a small yelp of pain. 'You rat!—that's unfair.'

'You didn't know how to get rid of him so I . . .'

'You sure know how to dig up old history. I was only seventeen. We were in high school.'

'You said you'd never forget me for it. You promised that you'd pay me back with your last breath. You vowed that if I ever needed help that you'd . . .'

'All right,' Samantha threw up her hands in the air. 'I give up. I surrender.'

'You'll do it then?'

Samantha sighed. 'The things I do for friends.'

Rachel gave her a quick hug. 'Sam—I love you and don't worry about the suit. It's very nice.'

'I'm going against my better judgment,' Samantha said grudgingly. 'I'm going to feel like a fifth wheel.'

Rachel's voice was soothing. 'No, you won't. It's only for lunch.'

'And this Harvey person isn't going to be happy to have me there. He asked *you* out.'

'Harvey doesn't have a possessive bone in his body—he'll be delighted to share himself between us. You'll see—Harvey will think two women are better than one.'

Samantha had slipped off the jacket of the suit and was unzipping the skirt. 'How did you get yourself into this mess? I don't understand why you agreed to go out with him in the first place.'

'It's a long story,' Rachel said cautiously.

Samantha pulled the skirt up over her head. 'Oh?—that sounds interesting. When do I get to hear it?'

'It's not important.'

Samantha ran quick fingers through her brown curls and studied Rachel's reflection in the dressing-room mirror. 'I'm getting peculiar vibes,' she said shrewdly. 'There's more going on here than meets the eye.'

Rachel had never been able to keep anything from Samantha, a state of affairs that went back twenty years to the time when they were both ten years old. Samantha had always been able to worm every secret out of her, from childhood gossip to adolescent crushes. They had lived next door to one another and had been best friends, a relationship that had withstood a separation during college and Samantha's disastrous marriage. They didn't get to see each other as often as they used to; doctoring took up most of Rachel's time and Samantha was rising rapidly through the hierarchy at the Department of Commerce where she worked as a policy analyst, but they talked on the 'phone frequently and got together at least twice a month.

'You're nosey,' Rachel said.

'Very.' Samantha pulled on a pair of jeans and a halter top. 'It's one of my best characteristics.'

'Says who?'

'Says me. I thrive on gossip and other people's affairs.'

'If you had a few of your own, you wouldn't have to live such a vicarious life.'

'Ouch,' Samantha acknowledged the barb. 'And *you* should talk. At least, I'm not celibate.'

Rachel raised an eyebrow. 'Oh, really? When was the last time you slept with a man?'

Samantha stared at her image in the mirror. 'In April.'

'Of what year?' Rachel asked sarcastically.

'Do I deserve this?' Samantha rhetorically asked her image. 'I take her shopping so she can find some clothes . . .'

Rachel grinned. 'And buy yourself a suit.'

Samantha ignored her. 'I give her moral support. I listen to sad stories. I agree to act like a duenna on an unwanted date.' She paused and then sighed. 'All right—it was April of last year. I've given up, Rachel, I really have. I've had my share. A philandering husband and so many bed partners I should have put a revolving door on my apartment.'

'Sam, that was two years ago.'

'I know, it was divorce mania. I had to prove something to myself and I did—that Bud was wrong, I wasn't frigid and I was attractive enough to catch a man. Unfortunately, I also learned that men will sleep with anything that's available. So big deal. Now, I'm more discriminating and guess what? There aren't any decent men out there.'

Rachel knew what Samantha was talking about; the only difference between the two of them was that she didn't care. Samantha, on the other hand, wanted to marry again; she believed in love and she thought that Ellie needed a father. The trouble was that most Washington men weren't interested in a home and stability. They were caught up in the world of power and politics where sex was easy and attractive women were a dime a dozen. Rachel knew the scene: the workaholic who needed a woman for a few hours' escape, the married man looking for a thrill, the politico wanting a diversion. For a woman like Samantha, a single mother who was looking for a spouse, Washington was a very difficult place to be husband-hunting.

A saleswoman called from outside the dressing-room door. 'Have you found what you wanted, Miss?'

'Yes,' Samantha answered. 'I'll be out in a minute.'

'Here,' Rachel said, reaching for the clothes hanging on a hook, 'I'll gather up the suits you don't want.'

'Just a minute. You still haven't told me what happened.'

'What happened where?'

Samantha walked to the door, spread her arms wide across it and said in a dramatic tone. 'Don't act so innocent. Speak or we'll be here forever.'

'You're impossible.'

'Come on, Rachel. You've not only foisted an unwanted lunch on me, you also look like hell.'

'Compliments, compliments.'

'I wasn't going to mention it, but you've forced my hand.'

Rachel took a deep breath and sat down on the stool, catching sight of her own image in the mirror. Samantha was right; she looked like hell. Her skin was pale beneath her make-up and there were circles a mile deep beneath her eyes. She could have blamed her exhaustion on a number of factors. Her car had broken down, the temperature had gone from hot to hot and muggy, she'd been working twelve hours a day non-stop, but none of it would have been true. She hadn't been sleeping well. She'd had trouble falling asleep when she went to bed and then, when she finally dozed off, she'd slept only restlessly. Rachel had never been one for sunrises but she'd witnessed several during the past week. They'd been predictably lovely, except that she hadn't been in any shape or frame of mind to appreciate them.

'All right,' she said. 'I met Harvey at a cocktail party at the Canadian Embassy last week.'

'And?'

'And Christopher is back, as Minister, and I got so flustered at the sight of him that I . . .'

'Christopher? Do you mean Christopher Blake?'

'Yes.'

Samantha had dropped her arms and was watching Rachel with a look that combined both astonishment and a profound sympathy. 'Oh, Rachel.'

'Do I have to spell it out?'

Samantha shook her head. She knew all about Christopher; she hadn't been living in Washington during Rachel's affair with him, but she'd returned in time to witness the wreckage afterwards. She knew the whole sordid story, from beginning to end, with the sort of detail that only close friends confide to one another.

'What did he say?'

'Not much. It was very . . . polite.'

'Is he married?'

Rachel gave her a startled look. 'I don't know . . . I mean I didn't ask and he didn't volunteer any information.'

'Does he want to see you again?'

'I don't think so.'

'What do you mean—you don't think so?'

'Well, he said something about getting in touch.'

Samantha was silent for a moment and then, 'He hasn't, has he?'

'No.'

'Do you think he will?'

Rachel shrugged and looked down at the floor. 'I doubt it. I think he was only being, well, cynical. There were other people there, and he was just having a very private joke.'

Samantha's voice was quiet. 'Do *you* want to see him again?'

Rachel's head came up quickly. 'You must be joking.'

Samantha kneeled down before her and took one of Rachel's hand in hers. 'Sorry,' she said, 'but I couldn't help wondering if you'd like to finish what you began ten years ago. It ended so abruptly.'

Rachel looked into Samantha's sympathetic eyes and knew that her question wasn't asked out of idle curiosity. Her affair with Christopher had never ended properly; it was still unfinished business as far as her psyche was concerned. Why else was she still a mass of contradictions, hating him and wanting him, all with the same breath? The dreams she'd been having that week came back to her, nightmarish mixtures of fact and fiction, of things that had happened long ago merging with things that had never occurred.

She'd dreamt of their lovemaking and then saw them walking together on the dunes beside her mother's new house in North Carolina. The ocean had pounded before them, wave upon grey wave breaking over the sand and sending up a salty mist. The roar of it had filled her ears, the sound matching the erratic beat of her heart. She had woken up from that one in a cold sweat to find her apartment silent, the pale light of dawn filtering in through her bedroom curtains. It hadn't meant anything, she told herself. Her mother had bought that house only two years ago; Christopher had never seen it. And they'd never walked beside an ocean either. It had been one of the things they'd planned on doing together, sometime, in the future. Except there hadn't been any future. Not for the two of them together.

'No,' she finally said, 'I'm better off if I never see him again. There was too much pain, too much hurt. I couldn't bear it.'

'Yes,' Samantha said sadly, 'I know.'

CHAPTER THREE

CHRISTOPHER was not enjoying the barbecue, although the weather was perfect and the setting was attractive. It was being held at the home of the Brakers, a small mansion tucked into one of the gentle hills that characterised Great Falls, Virginia, a bedroom suburb of Washington. It was a good house, the sort that foreign officers looked for when they moved to a new posting. Although it was fairly new, it had been designed to look as if it had been standing for a century at least. It was made of brick; there were white columns holding up the front portico; and a centre hallway ended in an oak-railed curving staircase that led up to the second floor.

Despite the air of old elegance, however, it came with all the modern appurtenances, an up-to-date kitchen, central air-conditioning and modern bathrooms. It was gracious, large and the main floor plan was perfect for holding cocktail parties without too much inconvenience. It was the sort of house that few foreign service officers could afford to own in Ottawa, but it was one of the perks of the system that, while on posting, they received enough of an allowance to rent a home that was considered 'representational'— suitable for parties and of a grandeur sufficient to main Canada's image abroad.

The back of the house had a huge patio with a stone-flagged floor and its own electrical barbecue. On it, Bill, a plump and genial host, had set half-a-dozen steaks to grill as well as hamburgers and hot dogs, while his wife Jeanine, tall and gracious, was making sure that everyone had drinks. It was a gathering strictly of Embassy people in Christopher's department. There

were about fifteen adults present and, seemingly, a small
army of children ranging in age from infants to pre-
adolescents. Babies toddled from chair to chair while
the older children raced around the Brakers' garden in
an endless game of tag. It was a very relaxed party for
everyone but Christopher. While it was in his honour
and the purpose of it, ostensibly, was that he could
meet everyone who worked for him along with their
spouses and families, the real motive was the Newmans.
Christopher had wanted to meet them in an informal
setting, and a barbecue had seemed like the perfect
solution.

This was one of the reasons Christopher wasn't
enjoying himself. He had rather hoped that the Newmans
would prove to be an unpleasant couple. He'd already
met Frank at the Embassy and found him intense but
earnest. It had been Mary who he'd been curious about,
expecting someone who was shrill, whiny and un-
attractive. Instead he'd found that she was pretty, short
and blonde and attractively plump, with a sweet smile
that was quite disarming. She was also very shy, and he'd
been forced to find a way to draw her into a conversation.
He'd done that by walking over to the pram that held the
Newmans' youngest child, a baby girl of six months old.
She'd been sleeping when he peered at her, her round face
framed by a white eyelet bonnet, one tiny fist curled up
above the satin hem of pink blanket. Her cheeks matched
the colour of the blanket and her lashes curved on her skin
in small, dark arcs.

'That's Lora,' Mary said. She had immediately
walked over to the pram when she had seen Christopher
by it. He'd known his interest in the baby would attract
her. There was nothing so strong or compelling as the
pride of a mother.

'She's very pretty.'

'Oh, thank you.'

Christopher leaned even closer. 'Who does she look
like?'

Mary smiled. 'Not Frank, I hope.'

Christopher stood up and grinned at her. 'Now what's wrong with Frank?'

'Well,' she said, 'can you imagine that nose on a girl?'

They both looked over at Frank, who was engaged in a conversation. He did have rather a beak of a nose along with a receding hairline. Christopher had to agree that it would be a disaster if baby Lora ended up the spitting image of her Dad. 'It would be nice if she took after you,' he said.

Mary immediately blushed and stammered something to the effect that Lora had almost no hair, but that they hoped she would be blonde like their other two.

'And which ones are those?' Christopher asked, looking out at the shifting mass of children.

'Billy's the one in the red shirt. He's five. And Sean is four. He's just behind Billy, holding on to his shirt.'

Christopher could see two tow-haired boys, tussling out on the grass. 'They look like a handful.'

'Boys are hard,' Mary said.

'Mmmm,' Christopher murmured sympathetically as if he'd spent his life bringing up a truckload of boys. 'Have you got them into good schools?'

As he had expected, this last question opened the floodgates and let out the torrent. Mary Newman might be shy, but when it came to talking about her children, she lost any reticence. Christopher heard it all, from the bad nursery school teacher to the bus that kept breaking down, from the chicken pox to the bed-wetting, from her isolation in the community (all the other women worked) to her inability to drive. *That*, Christopher could see as a disaster. In Ottawa, the public transportation was so pervasive that every part of the city was accessible by bus; suburban Washington, however, was different. Without a driver's licence, Mary was practically a prisoner in her own house.

By the time their conversation was coming to an end, Christopher felt that he had Mary Newman pegged. She was a homebody, tied up with three small children who took up a great deal of her time and energy. She was also too shy to make friends easily, and very lonely. Add all that to the problem of Frank not quite making it at work, and you had a woman who was susceptible to stress and anxiety. She had smiled as she talked, shrugging off the problems as if they didn't matter, but her attempt to act light-hearted failed. Christopher had seen her face knot up as she spoke, and her eyes had inadvertently given away most of her emotions. And, while she didn't say anything about wanting to go back to Ottawa, her homesickness would have been visible even to the most insensitive observer.

Frank had arrived then, flustered and embarrassed because his wife had tied up the Minister for so long. He was obviously worried that she'd said something wrong, out of place, or gauche. Not that he implied any such thing; he merely attempted to divert whatever conversation had been taking place.

'The steaks are almost done,' he said, staring from Mary to Christopher.

'I've been hearing all about your family,' Christopher said.

Frank's eyes widened from alarm. 'Mary, you didn't bore Christopher with stories about the children, did you?'

Christopher could see Mary starting to panic at the thought that she had said something that would harm Frank's career at the Embassy, so he quickly intervened. 'I like children,' he said and then nodded at sleeping Lora. 'Even babies.'

Frank hadn't looked convinced, but Mary relaxed a bit. 'I guess we should eat, shouldn't we?' she had said, giving him a quick glance and Christopher could see that her earlier shyness had come back in full force.

'Yes,' he had said. 'I think we should.'

All in all, it had been an unsettling conversation, and Christopher had the feeling that perhaps his original strategy had been wrong. He didn't know if the Newman's problems were solvable or if they would have to go back to Ottawa. It was a situation that would have to be resolved within the next few weeks whether he liked it or not. And talking to Mary at such length meant that he would never again see her simply as a name on a sheet of paper, a faceless body to be moved, an Embassy life that could be extinguished with one stroke of his pen. By being compassionate, he had now brought her into existence in his mind and imagination. Executioners, he realised with a dry touch of irony, lose their edge when they get to know their victims.

And there were other reasons why he wasn't enjoying the barbecue, although his unhappiness didn't show on his face. He wandered from person to person, asking the appropriate questions and looking as if he were fascinated with the answers. He was well aware, however, that there was a pair of eyes following him. The eyes had also tracked him at the Embassy, but they had been easy enough to ignore while he was working and in a different office. It was far more difficult out on this sunny patio where people were clustered together around the barbecue or by the table that was lined with salads and desserts.

So Christopher yielded to the inevitable and smiled at the owner of the eyes, Lucy Solvano, a young woman who worked as an assistant to the political attaché. She was only in her early twenties and beautiful in a dark and striking way. She had smooth olive skin, wide brown eyes and hair that gleamed like a black curtain down her back. She was the type of woman who would have attracted Christopher once when his inclinations ran to tasting each and every type of female beauty that came his way. But he'd grown bored with such liaisons and, besides, he'd set a policy for himself not to date women in his office. Life was easier and safer that way.

'Hello,' he said and then gestured at the empty lawn chair next to hers. 'Is this free or taken?'

Lucy smiled up at him. 'Free.'

'Do you mind?'

'No, of course not.'

Christopher sat down beside her and stretched his legs out beside hers, balancing his plate on his knees. He was wearing jeans and a T-shirt; she was in a yellow sundress that highlighted her dark beauty. 'Don't you like steak?' he asked, looking down at the uneaten portion on her plate.

Lucy smiled up at him. 'Actually,' she said in a whisper, 'I'm a vegetarian, but I didn't have the heart to tell the Brakers.'

'Are you really?'

'Yes.'

'Intermittently or faithfully?'

'Oh, faithfully. I'm a perfectionist. When I do something, I do it completely.'

'Like writing memos?' he asked teasingly.

'Especially memos. They take a special sort of dedication. Take yours for example.'

'Mine? Do we want to talk about my memos on a beautiful, sunny day like this?'

'Christopher,' she said, tapping him lightly on the arm with her hand, 'your memos are serious business.'

Although they were talking about nothing in particular, their tone was flirtatious and Christopher was well aware that Lucy's words were not about diets or memos. She was really talking in a subtle way about something else. Her eyes, her smile, the angle that her body leaned towards his were all part of the dialogue, a physical message far more blatant than her verbal one. I'm available, she was saying, and interested in you in a sexual way. It was a subterranean hum, a leitmotiv that filled in the pauses. Christopher had heard it many times before. It was a form of conversation that existed between a man and a woman when they were both alone and both hunting.

He smiled back at Lucy as she chattered idly on about the office, but the thought of sex had caused his mind to slip elsewhere. It had gone back in time to the cocktail party and to seeing Rachel again. The sight of her had physically hurt; he'd felt a pain twist around his heart as if a fist had suddenly gripped it. He hadn't known that such a pain could exist, and it had taken his breath away. She'd been so very beautiful standing there, more beautiful than he remembered: tall, shimmering in green, eyes wide and big, gold hoop earrings swinging against the backdrop of a tumble of honey-blonde hair.

And then the pain had receded, and Christopher had discovered that he wanted her. Just as he had ten years ago; intensely and fiercely. That had shocked him more than the pain. He'd become so jaded in recent years that his interest in women had waned and with it his sexual drive. He had thought it might be age, but on the night of the cocktail party, he had discovered that being thirty-five years old had nothing to do with his libido. His body hadn't forgotten Rachel in the least and was responding to the sight of her with the old passion, urgent and desirous.

Still he hadn't been able to resist putting in the knife and twisting it when he saw her. He knew what motivated him to suggest that they might get together again: a remnant of anger, the tag end of a frustration that had never been appeased. And he'd been amply rewarded. Christopher had seen Rachel's body grow rigid, had been able to read the panic in her eyes. He'd known then, beyond the shadow of a doubt, that their feelings were mutual. Rachel didn't want to see him again either. She'd been hurt, too; there was pain expressed in the sudden clenching of her fists as he looked down at her.

Then, suddenly, that power he had, the power to make her tremble, lost its edge. A terrible weariness had come over him, and he'd said goodbye, walked away from her. He'd been forced to smile at another stranger and to put on his diplomatic face, but all the while he'd been thinking, well, you've always wondered and now you know. She hates your guts. It's over. He had thought that knowledge would ease the resurgence of those old emotions, those old hurts. He didn't want to get mixed up with Rachel again. The pain that lingered was evidence that too much emotion still remained; too many cuts and slights and wounds. And, while his body might remember the best of their times, his mind recalled the worst. Their battles had been savage with no chance of compromise or peace. Christopher was well aware that the ten years had changed nothing except that both of them were even more rigidly set into careers that were diametrically opposed to one another. Rachel now had a medical practice; he was looking forward to promotions that would take him around the world.

But it wasn't over. No matter how much Christopher intended to put Rachel out of his mind, he'd not been successful. Her image came to him at odd moments, distracting him, interrupting his work. And the memory of her tormented him at night. He remembered times, places and events that he had not thought of in years. Visiting the National Zoo with Rachel at six o'clock in the morning so they could catch the Bengal tiger awake. Driving to New York late at night, her head on his shoulder, their two voices mingling as they sang. And the first time he had made love to her. Autumn leaves crackling around them, her body soft against his, grass caught in her hair. She had whispered to him, 'I . . . I've never made love with anyone before,' and he had touched her with a gentle and reverential care, believing that it would be a moment that neither of them would ever forget.

A week of sleepless nights and non-productive days had finally taken its toll. He'd screwed up an important negotiation with FCC, missed an important meeting with a notable at the Food and Drug Administration and left his briefcase, full of classified correspondence, at the Rayburn building after a briefing. His secretary, Margaret, had asked if he were feeling well; the Ambassador, who was far less sympathetic, had chewed him out. Christopher, who had never known what it was like to lose sight of a job for the memory of a woman, did everything he could to erase Rachel out of existence, short of blurring his mind with drugs. He ran two extra miles in the morning; he threw himself into work; drank at night before he went to bed in the hope of getting some sleep. But he was always awake in the small, dark hours of the morning, staring up at the black of the ceiling and *remembering*. Goddamnit, but he couldn't stop remembering.

In desperation, Christopher had finally 'phoned Rachel the day before the barbecue. It had been easy enough to get her home number through contacts at NIH without arousing any suspicions, but it hadn't been easy to lift up the receiver or punch in that number. He had wondered, too, as he heard the 'phone ring, if he weren't taking a lot for granted. She hadn't been wearing a wedding band, but she might have a lover or be living with someone. The thought of it made him pull the receiver from his ear, and he had almost put it back into its cradle when he heard her voice.

'Hello?'

He'd lifted the 'phone back to his ear. 'Rachel?'

Her voice had been wary. 'Yes?'

He ignored the thudding of his heart. 'It's Christopher.'

A long silence. 'Oh.'

He had started out obliquely, coming at her from an angle. 'It was a surprise to see you at the cocktail party.'

She cleared her throat. 'I didn't know you were back. I . . . hadn't thought you'd be there.'

'It brings back a lot of old memories.'

Wary again. 'Yes.'

'Rachel, I wonder . . .'

She spoke quickly, jumping in ahead of him, knowing what was coming. 'Christopher, I don't think . . .'

'. . . I'd like to see you.'

He could almost see her eyes widen, her head shaking a vehement negation. 'No . . . no, I don't think that would be a good idea.'

'We should talk.' Christopher sought for a meeting that would be safe, innocuous. 'Meet me for coffee. You pick the place, the day.'

'It's been too long. We don't have anything to say to one another.'

'You're wrong. It never finished.'

'What never finished?'

He paused and then said, 'You and me.'

Her voice was throaty, almost harsh. 'It's over. It's been over for years.'

Christopher could feel his disappointment; it was palpable and heavy like a weight hanging in his chest. 'Rachel, it's time to stop running.'

'Running? What are you talking about?'

'The way you left me. Running away.'

'Christopher, you left me.'

The old anger surged back, catching him off his guard. 'Christ, Rachel,' he said through clenched teeth. 'You know damn well that's a lie.'

Her voice trembled as if she, too, was suddenly caught in the grip of those old emotions. 'It isn't a lie. You may not have left me physically, that's true, but you were . . . gone, emotionally and mentally gone.'

'Rachel . . .'

'You can't change the past. Not now. Not because you want to.'

'I don't want to change the past. I . . . just want to understand it better.'

She started to speak and then her voice broke. 'Christopher, I can't talk to you anymore . . . I'm sorry

. . . I can't.' Then she hung up, the sound of the receiver clicking loudly in his ear.

Christopher had sat there, staring at the black, inanimate receiver of his telephone. Had she forgotten that night? The gleam of the lights on the wet pavement? The traffic that had swirled around them as he had gone after her? How could she have forgotten that nightmarish mix of screeching brakes, the curses of drivers, his own voice calling after her? She had run away from him; from his voice, his attempts to be reasonable, his logic. All right. Admittedly he'd been selfish and cold. But they could have discussed it like two mature adults. But they hadn't had the maturity then. The discussion had degenerated into a screaming match, and then she was gone, running away from him, her high heels clicking on the pavement.

'. . . and you've lived here before, haven't you?' Lucy was saying.

Christopher came back to reality with a sudden jolt. 'I was posted here before,' he said. 'Ten years ago.'

'Really? I didn't know that.'

'When Stevens was ambassador.'

'He's retired now, isn't he?'

'Yes.'

'Lucy really was a pretty thing, Christopher thought as they launched into a conversation about changes in the Embassy. Pretty and available. He could forget all his scruples about dating a woman he worked with and take her to bed tonight, use her to exorcise old ghosts. He'd been crazy to think that he should see Rachel again, and he hated himself for having tried. What had he expected? Open arms and a warm welcome? A willing body and a ready bed? He cursed the memories of Rachel that had driven him to the telephone; he damned his own lust which had lead him down the path of sweet illusion. What was next? he asked himself with irony. Furtive hanging-out by her apartment? 'Phone calls with silence and heavy breathing? Hell . . . Rachel was right. Of course, they were finished. He didn't blame her for not wanting to see him again. What was the point of raking up old coals and unleashing old angers? He would be better to bury them, to forget they ever existed. And what better way than in the sweet oblivion of another woman—another woman's soft body.

Christopher knew that Lucy would do just what he asked. She was his for the taking; a ripe morsel, a willing accomplice. They would make love and he would be able to sleep then, instead of tossing and turning, his skin too sensitive, every nerve remembering and *remembering*. All he had to do to get Lucy into bed with him was exert that extra bit of charm, glance at her in that intimate way that implied desire, and she'd willingly lay down before him, stripped and naked, dark and velvety against the white of his sheets. He brought his mind to bear on that image, tried to bring it into clearer focus and desperately willed it to arouse him. He smiled at Lucy, but the smile never reached his eyes. Their grey was dark and smoky, hinting at unhappiness, his hopeless despair.

Lucy Solvano thought she was doing well. She'd had her eye on Christopher since his arrival; she went for tall, dark men. And he wasn't married or divorced either; that was unusual for a man of his age, position and seniority. Of course, she wasn't the only woman in the Embassy to find Christopher attractive and eligible. The younger secretaries had been buzzing with gossip for weeks, and it had taken the concerted effort of a number of them to worm any information out of Margaret, Christopher's personal secretary. Margaret was close to retirement and generally close-mouthed, but a dozen free lunches had finally eased her reticence. She had admitted that as far as she knew Christopher had no love interest in his life. He hadn't taken any woman as his guest to a party and no woman had helped to host his own. Strange female voices didn't ring up the office, and he didn't leave messages for unknown women. And, while Christopher did not divulge his private life to his secretary, Margaret did keep his social calendar and knew that his weekday evenings were quite taken up with official business. The weekends, of course, weren't her affair, and she had absolutely no idea what he did with them.

That had been enough to send the aspirations of a number of secretaries into the stratosphere of hope and fantasy. Lucy was not quite so naïve as to think that Christopher was out hunting for women and would pick from the ranks below him. There were a lot of unattached women in Washington; women lawyers, lobbyists, consultants and researchers. Any number of them would be available to share professional interests and concerns. No, Lucy had understood that the competition for a man like Christopher would be enormous. He was good-looking, charming and politically powerful, a combination of qualities that, in in Washington, would put him in the class of extremely eligible bachelors.

Lucy rarely went to parties like this one; all the Embassy gossip and family talk eventually bored her. But when she heard that Christopher was coming, she had quickly accepted the invitation. Although Lucy often wrote memos for his attention or did research that he had requested, she'd had very little chance to talk to him on the job. She was far too subordinate for that. This was her one chance to make an impression, and now it seemed as if she was going to be successful. Christopher was eating with her; they'd been making idle and pleasantly flirtatious conversation, and every once in a while he threw an odd look at her, his grey eyes curious and speculative.

They'd fallen silent for a few moments and Lucy decided on her strategy. Of course, she'd accept if he asked her for a date, but if he suggested that they go out tonight, she'd also agree. Such an invitation would mean bed afterwards; Lucy knew that, she was nobody's fool, but she wasn't averse to the idea. Christopher was probably lonely; he was new in the city and didn't know any other women. Lucy wasn't necessarily interested in any long-term commitment; she simply liked to go to bed with men who were attractive and piqued her interest. And it didn't bother her that she and Christopher worked in the same office. Business was business and pleasure was pleasure. Lucy knew how to keep them quite straight in her head.

'Don't tell me you're a vegetarian, too,' she said teasingly, looking down at Christopher's plate where the steak lay uneaten. He hadn't touched much else either; not the coleslaw, the potato salad or the devilled eggs.

But Christopher didn't answer her, and Lucy glanced up at his profile, angular and dark against the blue of the sky. It seemed that he hadn't heard her; he seemed to be concentrating on something else. Lucy didn't like losing a man's attention and she looked in the direction of his gaze, across the patio, wondering what had struck Christopher as so fascinating that he'd forgotten she existed.

Nothing, she thought irritably, nothing that wasn't there before. The children were playing in the grass, the hammock was swinging empty in the breeze, and Mary Newman was lifting her baby out of the pram and putting it up to her shoulder. Lucy didn't see anything particularly exciting about a baby whose bonneted head drooped and swayed on its slender neck or who was so obviously drooling all over its mother's shoulder. So she tossed back her hair and turned to Christopher, smiling and expectant, only to discover that she might as well not have been there. He was oblivious to her, staring at that silly baby with an odd, speculative frown.

'Christopher?' she said.

His head swivelled around to her and his mouth smiled, but Lucy was far too astute about men not to know when she'd lost. His interest in her was gone, his attention merely polite. A baby, she thought with an angry, helpless frustration, a drooling, toothless, bald baby.

The office had been busy and Rachel had been busier. She'd attended a symposium on Infants at Risk at the National Academy of Science over the weekend, been part of a pot-luck supper with the other doctors in her practice on Sunday and arrived in the office on Monday to find two sales representatives waiting to talk about new drugs. Any opening in the appointment book was filled by noon, and Rachel's lunch was a hurried affair, a ham sandwich hastily eaten with a cup of coffee at quick moments between patients. She'd given a dozen vaccinations by two in the afternoon and taken more throat swabs than she cared to remember.

Her ears sang with the crying of babies. The noise in a paediatric practice was something she was still trying to get used to. Children played in the waiting room and cried when they came in to see her. She tried everything possible to make her small patients happy; she smiled and laughed and gave out lollipops, but it was hard to keep a kid grinning when the treatment required injections or blood samples. And she couldn't blame the children; she hated getting needles herself. She always had.

Right now, the Levin baby, two months old and with a head as bald as a melon, was lying on the examining table in nothing but a nappy and screaming, much to his mother's distress.

'He's like this a lot,' she was saying, wringing her hands together. She was a small woman with a worried frown between dark eyebrows. This baby was her first and only child, born after much trying and a difficult pregnancy.

Rachel ran a hand over the baby's abdomen, her fingers feeling for abnormalities. All the internal organs felt right, and he was obviously gaining weight. Despite the continual crying that was driving his parents around the bend, baby Levin was thriving.

'Colic is one of those catch-all words,' Rachel said over the noise of his crying. 'Some babys' digestive systems have a harder time maturing than others.'

'You mean he'll grow out of it?'

'They usually do.'

Rachel had often wondered why most adults persisted in thinking that infancy and childhood were, without exception, happy times. Babies like this one adapted to life with difficulty. And then there was the biological imperative that each child faced; to move, to crawl, to walk, to run. The way Rachel saw it was that babyhood was a time of work and struggle, of enormous gains made over seemingly impossible hurdles. Baby Levin had only barely learned how to hold up his head and he wasn't even close to having the muscular ability to turn over. In ten months, however, chances were that he'd be walking and even possibly saying a few words.

'Can't we give him anything to stop the pain?' Mrs Levin asked hurriedly, rushing to pick up her crying baby.

Because Rachel didn't have any children herself, she could never actually comprehend the tie between mother and infant, but she'd sensed the strength of that bond. A mother was often so sensitive, so aware of her baby, that she could almost feel the child's pain as if it were her own. Mrs Levin was one of those; Rachel could see it in the protective curve of her body as she lifted the baby up and put him to her shoulder, the soothing gestures of her hands on his back. Rachel knew there wasn't much use in telling her that babies grew even as they cried, that the seemingly frantic waving of arms and kicking of feet helped muscles strengthen or that the gulping of air and loud screams made lungs develop. Mrs Levin wanted something, anything, to stop her baby from hurting.

There was little that Rachel could do, and she wasn't the sort of doctor to recommend medications as placebos for worried mothers. But there was one angle that they hadn't explored with the Levin baby and, although it was a long shot, it would make the Levin parents happy to have something to work on.

'You're not breastfeeding, are you?' Rachel asked and, when Mrs Levin shook her head, she added, 'There's a slim chance he's allergic to formula.'

Mrs Levin patted her baby's back, and there was a moment of blessed silence. 'Allergic to formula?'

'To the cow's milk in formula. Some babies react to it. Now, there's a formula that's made from goat's milk.' Rachel scribbled the name of it on a prescription pad, tore off the paper and handed it to Mrs Levin. 'It might help. The one drawback is that it's expensive.'

Mrs Levin shook her head and gave a weary smile. 'I don't care if it costs a million dollars.'

'But it might not work,' Rachel said warningly. 'Lots of babies that have colic aren't allergic to anything. But call me after you've used it for a couple of days and let me known what's happening.'

The baby had started to cry again, and both women exchanged a rueful smile. 'Thanks, Dr Sims.'

Rachel passed Molly out in the hallway as she headed back to her own room. Each doctor had a suite that consisted of three examining rooms and an office, and the four suites surrounded a central waiting room which was filled with chairs, toys and play equipment and where the children were comfortable. It was a convenient, efficient and pleasant arrangement. The doctors didn't bump in to one another, and they each had a small area of privacy. Once a day, Rachel thanked Rob and her lucky stars for finding her a practice that was not only booming, but housed so well. She'd seen enough cramped doctors' offices to last her a lifetime.

'How's it going, Molly?'

'Two down, five to go. Two sore throats, a case of suspected measles, a small growth under one eye . . .'

'Who's that?'

'The Read child. And a new patient in for a well baby check with its father.'

That was unusual. 'No mother?'

'Honey chile, I didn't ask about his marital status.'

'Hmmmm—and that's it?'

'You want I should start booking patients during the dinner hour, Dr Sims?'

'God forbid.'

One sore throat turned out to be tonsils, the measles were nothing more than a rash and the small growth was benign, angular and formed of calcium. It would require surgery though and Rachel made the referral to a plastic surgeon. By the time she arrived at the door of the examining room for her last patient, the well baby, Rachel was exhausted, starving and looking forward to a quite evening in her apartment.

She was tired, physically and emotionally tired. She had not really thought that Christopher would get in touch with her again. He had been so aloof at the cocktail party, and the brush-off that he'd given her had seemed final despite that small, mocking suggestion that they get in touch sometime. It was as she had told Samantha; he'd merely been needling her, angling for a reaction. She'd been so positive that Christopher really didn't want to see her again that his 'phone call had come out of the blue, a weapon being hurled at her from a seemingly innocuous sky. She'd picked up the 'phone, expecting anything but that voice, that remembered deep voice. How many times had Christopher 'phoned her ten years ago? A hundred times? A thousand? Oh, she had known that voice immediately and felt her heart skip a beat, catch in its own rhythm and then start up again, unevenly, its drumming irregular and erratic.

Talk, Christopher had said. He had wanted to talk; he wanted to understand the past. It never occurred to her that Christopher's motives for wanting to see her again were anything but selfish, and his words had made her furious. She wasn't a psychiatrist, a counsellor or even a sympathetic friend. *She* didn't want to relive events that she'd spent years trying to forget, and she'd be damned if she was going to help Christopher if he was in the throes of some mid-life crisis. She had her own sanity to preserve, her own piece of mind. And then, he had implied that she had been the one to break off their relationship. As if he hadn't contributed with his utter and complete indifference to . . .

All right, she had run. She'd run with her heart pounding and her mouth dry. She had run because she had not been able to stand one more minute of his excuses, his reasons, his oh-so-very-rational motives. She had been so miserable and so angry that she'd wanted to hit him, to kill him with her bare hands. Rachel had never known such fury in her life before, and she had run from it. Away from the cute little restaurant with its red-and-white checked tablecloths, tiny carnations and waiters dressed in red pants and black waistcoats. Away from the curious faces of other diners who were listening to an argument that had turned into a shouting match. Away from the sound of her own voice, shrill and harsh.

She had run like the wind, hearing her own heels on the pavement and feeling the rain against her skin. She'd welcomed that dampness, turned her face up into it and prayed that it would rain harder. Harder, *harder* so that she could no longer feel the tears burn in her eyes and run down her cheeks, sliding along the side of her nose, catching at the turned-down corners of her mouth, dropping on to her hands. She had hoped it would rain forever; cleansing her, purifying her, erasing the salt taste in her mouth. Tears and rain: they had blurred together until she had barely been able to see where she was going. 'Rachel! Goddamnit it!' She had only known that she had to get away from him. 'Rachel! Come back!'

'He's a weird one,' Molly whispered.

Rachel came back to the realm of reality, to the door of an examining room, to the feel of the stethoscope swinging against her chest. She could see that Molly was angry, the rolls of fat under her chin shaking with indignation. 'Who?'

'The father in there. Didn't want to undress his baby. Wouldn't let me weigh her. He said he wanted to talk to you first.'

Rachel gave Molly a soothing pat on the shoulder. 'It doesn't matter. I'll do it.'

But Molly wandered off, muttering a litany of insults under her breath. 'Might have thought I was asking him to take off *his* nappy. All I wanted to do was weigh his precious morsel . . .'

Rachel smiled to herself. It didn't pay to outrage Molly. She was like the proverbial elephant; she never forgot an insult or a patient who refused to abide by her rules. Molly's running of the office made life easier for all the doctors, but woe to anyone who tried to buck the system. Disobedience or bad behaviour meant sulks and angry glances. But the doctors put up with it, and Rachel had discovered, early on, a deep affection for Molly. She was loyal, patient and worked harder than all of them. And when Rachel had first come into the practice, it had been Molly who had spent the hours with her going over procedures and talking about patients.

Rachel lifted the new patient's folder out of the metal holder on the door, noted the name—Newman—and brushed back a loose tendril of hair that had come out of the chignon at her neck. She was still smiling when she entered the room, shutting the door behind her, but the few words of welcome that she always spoke to a new patient died on her lips before she could utter them.

A man in a grey business suit sat on the stool by the examining table, dandling a baby on his knee. The baby was dressed in a pink terrycloth jumper with a teddy bear embroidered on the bib and her feet were enclosed in pink knit booties. She grinned at Rachel and stuck a fist in her toothless mouth.

'Hello, Rachel,' Christopher said.

CHAPTER FOUR

RACHEL was more than flabbergasted. She was struck
dumb by the sight of him. Her smile disappeared, her
brown eyes widened. She stared from Christopher to
the baby and then back again. A thousand fragmentary
thoughts raced through her mind. Married? . . . he had
never mentioned . . . well, she hadn't asked . . . she had
just assumed . . . of course, there was no reason . . . but
he hadn't wanted children . . . he had always said . . .

And all the while, Christopher was watching her, his
face perfectly poker straight as if there was nothing in
the world astonishing about his being in her examining
room with a baby on his knee.

Rachel finally found her voice. 'Is she . . . yours?'

'Mine? You mean—biologically mine?'

'What else would I mean?'

Christopher leaned over and retied the pom-pom on
the baby's bootie. 'Well, actually, she belongs to a
friend. I just borrowed her.'

Her heart did a surprising flip; her voice was a
disbelieving echo. 'Borrowed her?'

'Lora, meet Dr Sims. Dr Sims, meet Lora Newman.'
He picked the infant under her arms and raised
her in the air so that the small legs made tiny bicycle-
riding motions.

This was absurd. Rachel could make neither head
nor tail out of Christopher's presence in her office with
a borrowed baby. She closed her eyes for a second and
then opened them again as if she thought the apparition
of Christopher might disappear. He didn't though and
neither did the baby. Both of them were still there, large
as life.

Christopher was still talking, having put Lora back

down on his knee. 'You've done well,' he said, his glance taking in the freshly painted walls of the examining room, the gleaming sink, the fresh leatherette of the examining table. All the equipment was new, up-to-date and shining.

Rachel cleared her throat. 'Thank you.'

'It's what you wanted, isn't it?'

'Yes.'

'And I don't suppose it was easy.'

Rachel thought of the years of medical training, the hours of lost sleep, the endless cups of coffee and half-eaten sandwiches. She thought of the hard lessons she'd been forced to learn about her own fears and her own inadequacies. She'd hated inflicting pain; she'd shied away from confronting death.

'No,' she said slowly, 'it wasn't easy.'

'But it was worth it?'

Rachel lifted her chin. 'Absolutely.'

'No regrets?'

She knew what he was asking. Regrets—when had she not had regrets? Medical school had taken over her life, her thoughts and her emotions. The years that other women spent in satisfying personal needs had been put aside for her education and training. She had no husband, no children and no prospects of having any. Of course, she'd regretted what she had lost; she would have been abnormal if she hadn't. But life was full of choices not made and roads not taken. She'd long ago stopped agonising over them.

'None,' she said quietly.

Christopher nodded. 'No,' he said, 'I didn't think so.'

Rachel had been leaning against the door. Now, she straightened up. 'All right. Whose baby is that?'

'She belongs to one of the Embassy wives.'

'Does she really need a check-up?'

Christopher smiled for the first time, and it was the smile that Rachel remembered; boyish, light-hearted, slightly self-mocking. 'The dragon lady out there almost bit my head off when I wouldn't take Lora's clothes off.'

'If she doesn't need a check-up . . .'

Christopher patted one of Lora's fat knees. 'She's camouflage, aren't you, sweetheart?' Lora burbled, drooled and continued to suck on her fist. 'And you're a good girl, too.'

'Camouflage?'

'A disguise, protective cover.'

'I don't . . .'

His grin disappeared. 'Hell, Rachel, would you have seen me otherwise?'

Of course, she had known why Christopher was there, but she hadn't been able to believe it. His presence in her office was completely out-of-character with the man Rachel had seen at the Embassy; she simply couldn't connect this Christopher with the senior bureaucrat, the cool diplomat, the man whose office 'phone rang with important calls and whose briefcase held classified papers. Christopher borrow a baby so he could see her? It was unbelievable, ludicrous, *crazy*.

'You must be out of your mind,' she said.

'I told you—I think we should talk.'

She gripped the Newman folder close to her chest, but the anger she had felt towards Christopher at the cocktail party and during his 'phone call was no longer so intense or pervasive. It was hard, Rachel was discovering, to be furious at a man who not only had a baby on his knee but also seemed quite comfortable at having it there. She had seen plenty of men who didn't know the first thing about holding babies. Fathers who held their infants as if they were inanimate dolls or new daddies who stared down at their sons or daughters as if they were some sort of odd, strange species of animal, never before seen or encountered. Christopher wasn't like that at all. He held Lora as if she naturally fitted on his lap, one hand curving around her chest so that she wouldn't wriggle forward and the other resting gently against her back. You would have thought that Christopher, the man who had said that he never wanted children, had been holding six-month-old babies on his lap since the beginning of time.

'And I told you,' Rachel said, clearing her throat. 'I don't think it's a good idea.'

'Look, Rachel, I wouldn't be here if I didn't feel strongly that there were things left unsaid by both of us. You walked, ran, out of my life . . .' he raised a hand to stop her objection, '. . . and maybe your reasons were justified. I've never really been able to sort it out.'

She took a deep breath. 'I don't want to sort it out.'

'Why not?'

'I can't see the point of digging through the past.' Rachel had thought a lot about what Christopher had said in his 'phone call, and now she had her defence ready. 'I don't need to understand what happened. It isn't going to change my life now or explain my personality any better or help me figure out how to deal with the future. I don't need any rehashing of old . . . problems.'

He was quick. 'You weren't going to say that, were you?'

'What?'

'Problems. That's not what you mean, is it? You're afraid of going back, afraid that it will hurt.'

The old anger flared briefly. 'All right. You don't have to torture me to get it out. Of course, it would hurt. I hurt when it happened and I . . .'

Rachel couldn't finish, but Christopher did it for her. 'And you still feel the pain?' he asked softly.

'I don't want to . . .'

'You said it was over, but it isn't. Don't you see?' He leaned forward, the harsh angularity of his face close to Lora's soft, rounded features. 'That's why we should talk. Because it isn't over.'

Their eyes met over the baby's innocent, downy head; brown to silvery-grey in an arc of silent knowing, of unwilling agreement. It wasn't over; Christopher was right. It had never been over: not for her, not for him. There had been no end, no finish, no resolution. Neither of them had been able to properly pack away the emotions of that love affair. The boxes wouldn't shut, the locks wouldn't close. Tail ends of feelings trailed in their souls like unwanted shadows, and Washington with its population of three million didn't feel big enough to hold both of them. There would be other accidental meetings, chance encounters engineered by a careless fate, forcing both of them to relive moments that should have been over and done with.

But Rachel still intended to turn Christopher's suggestion down. No, she wasn't angry with him any longer; that emotion seemed to have run its course, but she couldn't see the point of it. What was there to say? They no longer had anything in common except the dregs of the past, and she was convinced that coming to conclusions at this late date would not change her future. Besides, she was too busy, too involved in her own work and far too content in her own life to have the time to . . .

An old image surfaced. It was odd that that one should have come swimming to the forefront of her consciousness at this moment, rising up from happier times after being submerged so long beneath those memories of fighting and bitterness, of crying and running away. The image came from a time when she and Christopher had just started sleeping together, when his character was still unfolding before her like a gift enclosed in endless sheets of wrapping paper and miles of ribbon. He had a personality, he had told her, that was typically English Canadian; serious, law-abiding, reserved and polite. But beneath that, she often caught glimpses of another man, one who was quixotic, charming, funny and capricious, and it was the glimpses that enchanted her.

They were not yet living with one another and had planned an informal date; a movie and then a beer and pizza. But, at the last minute, Rachel changed her mind. She had passed an important exam in Organic Chemistry and felt like celebrating. After making a reservation at one of Washington's most prestigious restaurants, she called Christopher at his apartment.

The 'phone rang at least ten times and then, 'Hello?'

'Chris, it's Rachel. Where were you?'

'I was in the shower.'

'Oh, I'm sorry.'

'That's all right. The carpet needs a watering. Makes it grow faster.'

'Don't be such a drip.'

Christopher groaned in her ear, laughed and then said, 'Want to come over and dry me off?'

Rachel lover her telephone conversations with Christopher. They were flirtatious and full of sexy innuendos. 'Why should I want to do that?' she asked, a little too innocently.

'There's a cosy little number I've learned to do with a towel,' Christopher said with a lazy drawl. 'You start at the neck, rub gently over my chest, stroke lightly over my abdomen and then work your way down to my . . .'

The word that he said wasn't printable. Rachel laughed and said warningly, 'I'm going to call the State Department and have your visa revoked. Shame, shame.'

'Well,' he said, his voice filled with mock-hurt, 'if you won't come over and give me some tender, loving care, what do you want? Won't I be picking you up in an hour?'

'We're going to dinner at Chez Marcel.'

'We *are*?'

'I've decided,' she said firmly.

'Aye, aye, sir. And is there a reason that Your Ladyship has decided to change the place of venue?'

'We're celebrating.'

'Celebrating what?'

'A ninety-five on my Organic Chemistry exam.'

Christopher knew what that meant. Both of them had been living with the threat of Rachel's exam hanging over their heads for the past month. 'Well, hallelujah and pass the molecules.'

Rachel assumed a commanding, regal voice. 'And a jacket and tie, please.'

Christopher knew how to affect a real southern accent. 'Yes, Ma'am.'

Rachel wore her favourite dress, a sexy black number that revealed more than it covered. She'd put her hair up, leaving several honey-blonde tendrils to curl along her cheeks, and slipped her feet into a pair of black sandals with heels so high that her derrière swayed invitingly when she walked. Her mother, Phyllis, raised her eyebrows when Rachel had come down to the living room.

'Big date?' she'd asked.

'With Christopher—at Chez Marcel's.'

'Well, well.' If Phyllis suspected at this time that Rachel was sleeping with Christopher, she never voiced her suspicions. Their relationship was like that; Phyllis had always treated her daughter as if she were another adult. She'd respected her wants, her accomplishments and her integrity, and she rarely probed or asked embarrassing, unwanted questions. Rachel knew that her mother would never ask her about Christopher; she'd wait until the words were ready to come of their own accord.

'How do you like the dress?' Rachel whirled around.

'You look smashingly seductive. I'm not sure Christopher will know what hit him.'

Rachel threw her arms around her mother. It wasn't a hard act; Phyllis was three inches shorter than Rachel without the heels and weighed fifty pounds less. She was a tiny woman with greying dark hair, snapping blue eyes and a strong will. She was a painter who had supported herself and Rachel by taking freelance nursing jobs whenever the need for money arose. Although there had been some insurance money after Michael Sims had been killed in a car crash, there hadn't been enough to raise a daughter and still put her through medical school. Rachel knew how hard her mother was working to make her dream possible.

'You like Chris, don't you, Mom?' she asked anxiously.

'He's very nice.'

'No, really. What do you *think*?'

Phyllis pushed her away and smiled at her. 'Does it matter what I think?'

'Of course, it does,' Rachel said and then added dramatically, 'it's the most important thing in the world.'

'Really, Rachel—the most important?'

'I *want* you to like him.'

Phyllis looked at her daughter's face, flushed with excitement, her brown eyes wide and shining. 'I do,' she said.

'I can hear the "but" in your voice,' Rachel said sulkily.

Phyllis sighed. 'Well, if you want my opinion, I think he suits you well, but I'm not sure he'll make you happy.'

Rachel stepped back, a frown pulling her eyebrows together. 'What do you mean—he won't make me happy?'

'I didn't say—won't. I said that I'm not sure he will.'

But that was heresy as far as Rachel was concerned, and she didn't ask Phyllis any more questions. Christopher not make her happy? Why, he was making her ecstatic! Her world was brighter and lovelier just because of his presence in it. She was in love with him and he was in love with her. Everything about him made her happy; his oh-so-serious view of life, his slow smile, the sideways glance of his grey eyes, his hands on her body. Yes, especially that. Lovemaking: long and dream-filled hours together in Christopher's four-poster bed, but then Phyllis didn't know about that. Rachel wasn't ready yet to tell her.

A car door slammed outside the house.

'That's Christopher!' she said, spinning around and rushing to the door, opening it before he could ring the bell. She would have raced into his arms, but her forward motion stopped abruptly, her mouth forming an astonished O.

Christopher bowed at the waist and extended an arm, backwards, towards his car. 'Madam, your chariot.'

'I don't believe you,' she said breathlessly.

Christopher smiled past her. 'Hello, Mrs Sims. Nice evening, isn't it?'

All Phyllis did was raise her eyebrows again. 'Delightful,' she said.

Rachel once more let her disbelieving gaze run over Christopher's attire. He was wearing black shoes, dark socks and the slacks to his blue suit, but from there up any resemblance he had to a man dressed in good taste disappeared. Oh, he had on the jacket to the blue suit; that was true, and also a tie with blue and brown stripes. But the latter was knotted around his bare neck and hung down his naked chest, bisecting the pectoral muscles, the triangle of dark chest hair. A slight breeze lifted the end of the tie and flapped it over his navel.

'Where's your shirt?' she finally stammered.

'Darling,' Christopher said, all devilish innocence, 'you just told me to wear a jacket and tie.'

It was this episode from her past that caught in Rachel's memory, that and the ridiculous image of Christopher half naked, standing on the doorstep of her mother's house, grinning his head off at her. That Christopher had been so different from the man who had forced her to run away from him, from the man at the cocktail party with his severe and forbidding air. That Christopher had a quirky sense of humour that shone through his serious side the way that rays of the sun gleam through clouds. He was capable of outrageous absurd acts—like showing up on her doorstep half dressed, like arriving in her office with a borrowed baby. She wouldn't mind, she thought, seeing that Christopher again and was immediately confused. Two weeks ago she'd hated the very idea of being near him; two minutes ago she'd had every intention of turning down his invitation. Would the real Christopher please stand up? Oh, hell, she thought in frustration, will the real Rachel stand up and make up her mind.

'All right,' she said slowly as if the words were being dredged up and dragged out of her. 'I'll meet you.'

Was he relieved? Happy? Triumphant? It was hard to know. She'd forgotten how capable Christopher was at hiding his emotions when he wanted to. His face could be a mask, his expression enigmatic. 'Fine,' he said. 'You name the place and time.'

Rachel calculated quickly. Her days were busy, her weekends her own. 'For dinner—sometime during the week,' she said and then added quickly, 'at a restaurant.'

He merely nodded his head in acknowledgment, and Rachel could see that the cool, formal Christopher was back, resuming his professional role. A stranger would have thought that they were diplomats negotiating a trade treaty instead of ex-lovers discussing a social engagement.

'And don't expect anything,' she said warningly.

Christopher shifted Lora from one knee to another. She was a very accommodating baby; she grinned at him and then went enthusiastically back to sucking on her fist. 'What should I expect?' he asked, his eyes studying her face and its sudden flush.

'A . . . a return to the past.'

He didn't smile, he merely acted as if he were sorting

out a point of law. 'When you say a return to the past, do you mean sleeping together?'

Rachel had meant everything; the whole kit and caboodle of an affair, the full-blown emotions, the incredible highs and the devastating lows, but Christopher had, quite simply, ignored all the frilly packaging and gone straight for the core of the matter. 'Yes,' she said, wishing that she could be as cool about it as he was.

His voice was casual. 'That wasn't what I had in mind.'

Christopher might be used to the making of subtle pacts and agreements, but Rachel didn't have that kind of experience. She rushed on, nailing down the details, making sure that the ground rules were firmly established, the territory well laid out. 'I'm not in love with you anymore.'

The grey eyes were carefully non-committal. 'No.'

'And nothing has essentially changed. There is still no way that anything between us could ever come to ... anything,' she finished lamely. She was already regretting her agreement to see him and wondering if there were some way of extricating herself out of an uncomfortable situation.

'No, it couldn't,' Christopher said, standing up and putting Lora to his shoulder. The baby grabbed a handful of his hair and, wincing, he gently opened her fist. 'Would Thursday night be okay with you?'

Rachel watched as the baby rested her cheek against Christopher's broad shoulder and he cupped the back of her head with his hand. 'I ... I guess so.'

'I'll pick you up at eight.'

'Yes,' she said, bemused once again by the sight of the baby, soft and pink and helpless, being held in Christopher's arms, a knitted bootie pressing against the lapel of his grey suit jacket, a fat fist tiny against the expanse of his chest.

'Good.' He was gone then, leaving her in the middle

of the examining room, staring at the opened door, not knowing quite what had happened to her, not understanding what she had agreed to.

'Dr Sims? Dr Sims?'

Rachel came to and blinked at the sight of Molly, filling the doorway with her bulk. 'Yes?'

'We've got a bit of an emergency.'

The woman in her fled as the doctor came back in force. 'An emergency?' Molly didn't use such a word unless a crisis was in full force.

'The Hale boy swallowed some . . .'

She was out of the room, rushing past Molly and heading towards the telephone, every thought of Christopher gone. It wasn't until several hours later when she was finally home and crawling into bed, her body exhausted, her mind swimming with fatigue, that she remembered something odd—that Christopher had not answered her the way she would have expected. He hadn't said the logical thing, the proper retort, the response that would have forever soothed her anxieties about seeing him again. She had made her position very clear; she'd told him that she didn't love him. She would have thought . . . wouldn't it have been likely that? . . . Rachel shook her head tiredly as she turned on the pillow and bunched it under her head. She was imagining things, setting up paper tigers. So Christopher hadn't said that he didn't love her anymore. So what? It was quite obvious that he didn't.

Wasn't it?

The lunch with Harvey Campbell was a smashing success, at least for two out of the three participants. It helped that Harvey's choice was impeccable; the small French restaurant was tucked away in a corner of Georgetown, the food was delicious and the atmosphere pleasing. Outside it was hot and the streets were crowded with tourists peering into the expensive boutiques that lined Georgetown's streets. Inside, it was cool and elegant with drooping ferns and white linen tablecloths and the discreet sound of conversations coming from tables that weren't placed too closely together. Waiters hovered nearby, appearing when wine glasses needed refilling or plates required removal and disappearing again, as silently as they had come.

Harvey was, as Rachel had predicted, in fine fettle. He hadn't blinked an eyelid when she'd arrived with Samantha in tow; in fact, he was clearly delighted to be entertaining two women instead of one. He'd complimented them extravagantly—on their beauty, their dresses, their personalities. And it had helped immensely that he and Samantha had struck an immediate chord of amiable wrangling. They'd argued with zest over politics, local and federal; a movie they'd both seen; modern versus representational art; and foreign policy. Harvey's eyes gleamed behind his round glasses; Samantha was having the time of her life. Neither of them noticed that Rachel merely picked at her breaded artichoke salad, her veal sautéed with mushrooms and wine and her carrots vinaigrette.

'Harvey, you're a damn chauvinist. If there's one thing I can't stand it's a man who thinks he knows the answers to everything.'

'Samantha, my love, I simply have an intuitive grasp of the machinations of government. Just because I immediately saw through your boss's small plan to block trade with Saudi Arabia. It simply fits into the Republican scheme of . . .'

Rachel had tuned in and now she tuned out. Politics had never fascinated her; a severe failing in a town that thrived on political gossip and speculation. Her mind slipped to the office. The Levin baby had not responded to a change in formula, she'd ordered blood tests for the Craig girl—that didn't look good and Rachel was afraid of the results—and there were a dozen insurance forms to be filled out when she went back after lunch. Then she had the dinner with Christopher coming up.

Fortunately, she had enough discipline to keep that worry firmly in the back of her mind where it wouldn't interfere with her work. However, now that she wasn't doing anything except idly pushing a fork around her plate, it had started to insinuate itself into her thoughts, a snake of anxiety weaving among all her other concerns and fears.

'She didn't hear a word,' Samantha was saying. 'Are you with us, Rachel?'

'Just thinking.'

'Never try to hold a long conversation with a paediatrician,' Harvey confided to Samantha. 'Their thoughts are constantly on streptococci.'

'Is that some sort of linguini?'

'Ah, Samantha.' Harvey took her hand and lifted it to his lips. 'We must have a long talk about subjects on which you're incredibly ignorant.'

Samantha snatched her hand out of his grasp and turned to Rachel. 'Tell me where you found this man again—so we can send him back.'

'The Canadian Embassy,' Harvey said. 'And I'm not returnable.'

'Too bad,' Samantha said tartly. 'Now, Rachel, what's on your mind?'

Rachel smiled. 'Nothing serious.'

Samantha winked at Harvey. 'You have to learn how to translate Rachelese. I've had years of experience and that last comment meant that something is bothering her.'

Now Harvey picked up Rachel's hand and stroked it. 'Rachel, sweetheart, what is it? Cranky children? Too many sore throats? The paediatric blues? Come on, tell Dr Campbell and he'll cure all.'

Rachel removed her hand. 'I thought you were a haematologist.'

'You see,' Harvey said to Samantha. 'What can you do with someone who has such a vocabulary? She shoots me down every time I open my mouth.'

'Perhaps,' Samantha said archly, 'you shouldn't talk so much.'

Harvey was having the time of his life. He beamed at Rachel and he beamed at Samantha. And Samantha wasn't doing too badly either. She was glowing as if Harvey's ridiculous remarks and outrageous flirtations had sparked something within her. The fun they were having made Rachel feel a little left out and slightly sad, but she just couldn't find the energy or the stamina or the will to join in with them. Life looked too sombre right now, the pressures of work piling on her, the apprehension she felt about seeing Christopher crowding out any lighter emotion. For the first time since she'd graduated from medical school and entered into a practice, Rachel wished that she didn't have to go back to the office. And she had the sudden urge to get away from it all, to hop on a plane heading anywhere as long as it was far from Washington and the constraints of her life, its parameters strictly measured by hospital rounds, by appointments, by crying children and, now, by a man that she had left ten years ago. A man who had the ability to make her laugh the way no one else could, but who had also broken her heart beneath the bruising weight of his cruelty.

'I beg your pardon.'

Tom Ferguson's eyes looked as if they were going to pop out of his head, and Christopher felt like cursing, only it wasn't his style to swear at subordinates.

'That's the way it's going to be,' he said coldly.

Ferguson cleared his throat and rearranged the papers in his hands. 'All right. I'll let Braker know.'

But it wasn't all right, and Christopher could tell from Ferguson's quickly concealed expression that he hadn't expected the decision on the Newmans to go in the direction it had. It made Christopher wonder just how much pressure Braker had applied to Ferguson and just how bad Frank Newman's work really was.

Well, it didn't matter anymore. He'd made up his mind, and there wasn't a damn thing anyone could do about it. Oh, he supposed that Ferguson and Braker could try to go over his head to the Ambassador, but that wasn't likely. As Minister, he could put the screws on their careers; they wouldn't dare rock the boat over an insignificant nobody like Newman.

'Is that all, Tom?'

Ferguson looked up from his perusal of his nails. 'I just wondered . . . I mean, I can't figure out how . . .'

He paused and Christopher gave him an impatient look. 'Yes?'

'If you feel that it's his wife that's the issue, how do you plan to . . . ah, solve her problems?'

'There's a couple of possibilities.' Christopher swivelled in his chair and looked pointedly down at a file on his desk.

Ferguson was nothing if not quick to the draw. He stood up. 'Well, in that case, I'll be seeing you later. We have that meeting with the finance people.'

Christopher barely looked up. 'Right. See you at two.'

He didn't let out a sigh until Ferguson was gone, the door closing behind him. Then Christopher sat back in his chair and stared up at the ceiling, cursing himself for being ten times a fool and an impulsive bastard into the bargain. Of course, Frank Newman should be sent back to Ottawa. Even the most novice foreign service officer could see that. The man hadn't adapted well, the pressure was getting to him and he was so damned nervous that he was driving everyone around him crazy. The fault lay somewhere between the flaws in his own personality and his family problems; no one could judge precisely which had the worst influence.

Christopher should have made the hard decision and eased the Newmans out of Embassy life in the kindest way possible—quickly. But he hadn't. He'd let impulse get the better of him, and now he couldn't act in the best interests of the Embassy and, perhaps, the Newmans. When he'd seen Mary lift her baby out of the pram at that barbecue, the idea had come swooping down on him. He hadn't been able to get rid of it either. Poor Lucy Solvano; she'd lost him then and they'd both known it. Their conversation had limped on, her vivacity eventually dulling beneath his obvious indifference. The promise of a pleasurable sexual engagement had eventually died a natural death, and she'd had the poise to get up and leave then, still smiling and still letting Christopher know, in that subtle way, that if he changed his mind she was still ready, available and willing.

He had wanted to change his mind; he would have given his right arm to take Lucy home and screw the living daylights out of her. He would have forgotten Rachel then and any crazy idea that came winging into his head. But he'd let Lucy go. He wasn't sure, of course, but he had the suspicion that, even given her willingness and her beauty, he wouldn't have been able to make love to her or, if he did, that he wouldn't enjoy it all. Not with Rachel in his head, her image interfering with his desires and obliterating any woman that he saw. He'd tasted then the bitterness of imagined failure and he hadn't liked it one damn bit.

And the voice of his subconscious had grown louder, clamouring at him and plaguing him, a mental gadfly that kept on stinging. 'Borrow the baby and show up at Rachel's office. She'll have to talk to you then.' He'd tried to ignore it; he'd said to himself that it was absurd, ridiculous, and irresponsible. He wasn't twenty-five anymore; he had his dignity to consider and his position. How could he ask Mary if he could take her baby? What would she think? And, if he did it, how could he fire her husband and send him back to Ottawa? Christopher tried to ignore that inner voice, but it had an unceasing grasp on his imagination. He could envisage that scene in Rachel's office; her astonishment and her delight. Oh, he knew she wouldn't show it, but he also knew that, inside, she would be amused by what he had done. For some reason, Rachel had brought out in him, and still did, it seemed, a wish to be funny, to tickle her fancy. It was a facet of his character that Christopher hadn't known existed until he had met Rachel.

Christopher didn't pity himself, and he wasn't so introverted that he agonised about the past, but his background was one of grinding poverty and a constant scramble to get out of it. There had been little humour in his family; life had been far too hard for smiling. His father, the town drunk, had been pitiable, and his mother had spent long hours cleaning other people's houses and ironing other people's clothes. But she'd had a strong, religious faith and a belief that Christopher's life would be different than her own. It was a tribute to her that he'd gone as far as he had, and one of his proudest moments had been the day he'd brought her to Ottawa, installed her in a condominium he'd bought for her and made sure that she didn't ever have to work again. Pride had been the backbone and the salvation of the Blakes, mother and son. Laughter, however, had been lost.

Rachel had shown Christopher that, hidden beneath his granite-like determination to succeed, was a source of fun, a rippling stream of humour that came occasionally to the surface, glinting in the sun of her personality. He had loved to watch her look of surprise, that astonished blink, and then her smile of appreciation. She had a smile that started at the corners of her mouth, made her nose wrinkle and then ended up warming her wide brown eyes. And when she laughed . . . well, the world changed when Rachel laughed, a silvery sound that cascaded around his ears, full and bell-like. Through those smiles and laughter, Christopher had learned about himself, but it was a lesson that remained in the past. No other woman had ever been quite able to reproduce it.

'Mr Blake?'

Christopher came out of his reverie and saw Margaret standing in the doorway. 'Yes?'

'Ottawa on the line. Mr Miller wants to talk to you about the Prime Minister's trip to Washington in the autumn.'

'I'll pick it up in a minute.'

Well, there was no going backwards, no erasing the idea, the persistent inner voice, the conviction that he'd never be able to enjoy making love to another woman until he got Rachel out of his system somehow, nor the final impulse that had made him reach for the 'phone and call Mary Newman. Her surprise had been predictable as was her hesitation to lend out the one and only Newman daughter. He had promised to keep Lora in safe-keeping, explaining that he needed her for a joke he wished to play on an old acquaintance. Mary had seemed convinced by that and, no doubt, her agreement also hinged on the knowledge that Christopher was her husband's boss. She'd warned him all about the less than civilised habits of babies, not quite believing that he'd still want to go through with it, but he had insisted and the scheme had gone off without a hitch. He'd returned Lora to her mother along with a gift as thanks—a large blue-and-white stuffed giraffe that Lora had immediately drooled over.

And the idea had worked even if it meant that he now had to come up with some brilliant way of making the Newmans fit into an alien environment. Rachel was willing to see him—admittedly on neutral territory—but that was a start. She'd been very careful to lay down all the ground rules, and he'd known better than to challenge them. So he'd agreed to everything, even her assertion that they couldn't return to the past or resume a sexual relationship. He had his own thoughts about that, but he couldn't voice them. And as for her statement that she no longer loved him, Christopher accepted that. He hadn't believed that she would still feel about him as she had in the past. Hell, he didn't feel the same way about her, either. That cornucopia of emotion had not been endless; it had flowed and flowed until there was little left of the richness that had once existed. Christopher was quite sure that his present feelings towards Rachel comprised lust, curiosity and, oddly enough, a simple sort of affection. That was all, and it didn't add up to love.

He picked up the 'phone. 'Hello, Bill? Christopher Blake here.'

'Chris, you old son of a gun. Are you getting Washington ready for the Canadian invasion?'

'I'm trying, but I can't convince them to put artificial snow down on the White House lawn. I told them it would make the PM feel at home, but they didn't buy it.'

Bill laughed and Christopher sat back in his chair, one part of him listening to the 'phone conversation, the other part still on Rachel. Hell, when he got right down to it, he didn't know what love was anyway. He couldn't define it, measure it or taste it. Maybe it didn't exist; maybe it was a figment of the imaginations of songwriters and novelists. And what he'd felt for Rachel in the past?—that fell in the category of infatuation, puppy love, and romantic, adolescent yearning. No, he didn't love her now; of that, Christopher was positive. What he felt was far cruder than that. He wanted to get Rachel in a bed somewhere, naked and beneath him. The old sexual itch, the typical masculine urge: that's all it was. Not love. Never.

CHAPTER FIVE

THE dinner was going surprisingly well. Rachel hadn't thought it possible for her to be sitting across from Christopher, the width of a small table between them, and actually feel relaxed and comfortable. But Christopher had made every effort to see that she was having a good time, and his efforts had paid off. The light-hearted conversation and the quiet ambiance of the restaurant were having the required effect. Rachel found herself discussing her work with animation, smiling at a joke, even laughing on the occasion. She had forgotten what a nice date Christopher could be. He wasn't in the diplomatic corps for nothing; he knew how to carry on a conversation, draw out his partner and make sure the atmosphere was amiable and pleasant. He was also the kind of man who got the best table, the waiters' instant attention and the chef's best effort.

'This is delicious,' Rachel said, tasting her salmon poached with dill. The restaurant, a new one in the District, specialised in seafood and its atmosphere was reminiscent of an old sailing ship with planked walls, port holes for windows and a huge ship's wheel hanging over the bar. 'How did you find this place?'

'Someone from Congressional Research took me here for lunch.'

'You haven't had any trouble adjusting back to Washington life, have you?'

Christopher shrugged, his shoulders broad in the fine cut of his grey herringbone jacket. 'It's quiet after Beirut.'

'You were in Beirut?'

'For three years.'

'And before that?'

'Mexico City, Paris.'

'No rest and recreational stays in Ottawa?'

He smiled at her. 'They were short. I'm not the rest and recreational type.'

'No, I've noticed.' The waiter came by, lifted the wine bottle out of its container of ice and filled their glasses again. Rachel waited until he was gone and then continued, 'And no thought of marriage or family?'

Christopher had lifted his goblet and now he glanced at her over its rim. 'No, I've not been interested. What about you?'

It was Rachel's turn to shrug, and she did it very eloquently, her shoulders pale and gleaming beneath the black straps of her dress. 'No time to think about it. Medical school was all-consuming.'

'And now?'

She smiled at him. 'There's still not much time. My practice keeps me very busy. I'm afraid I'm even on call tonight. My partners and I trade weeks and this one was mine.'

'On call?'

Rachel reached into her bag and pulled out a small and narrow black box. 'If it starts beeping, I head to the nearest 'phone and track down the emergency. It's efficient and very obtrusive.'

'Are you trying to tell me we won't get through dessert?'

'There's no telling. Some nights it's quiet; others are busy.' Rachel patted the box and slipped it back into her bag. 'So far it's been very good, but I'd keep my fingers crossed.'

Christopher had been watching her as she spoke, noting her happy smile. 'You really enjoy paediatrics, don't you?'

'I love it. It's challenging and rewarding.'

'I'm proud of you,' he said.

Rachel gave him a surprised look. 'Are you?'

'Of course. Ten years ago, I thought your wish to be a doctor was a pipe dream. I didn't think you'd be able to do it. You didn't seem serious enough. You didn't have either the guts or perseverance to get through medical school.'

'I didn't until . . .' Rachel paused, suddenly realising what she had been about to say.

'Until what?' Christopher asked gently but, when she didn't answer, he supplied the missing words. 'Until we broke up?'

She lifted her glass to him in a mock toast. 'To Christopher—whose departure to Paris taught me strength and independence.'

His mouth twisted, and he leaned forward. 'Rachel, if I could go backwards in time, if I could change what I had done, I would gladly . . .'

But she couldn't listen to the regretful words, to the sadness in his voice. For a long time after Christopher had gone to Paris, she had dreamed that he would return and beg her forgiveness, but now that an old fantasy was coming true, Rachel discovered that she couldn't bear it. 'It's over and done with,' she said brightly. 'Now, let's talk about you.'

'Me?'

'You,' she said firmly.

Christopher shrugged and then smiled. 'All right. What do you want to talk about?'

'Mmmm—women,' she said.

'Rachel. Really. Now, why did I think you'd want to talk about fishing rights off Nova Scotia?'

'Because you're a coward.'

'Me?' he said again.

'Talking about fishing rights is very safe, isn't it?'

'Not when you're negotiating with the Department of Commerce.'

'But I'm not the Department of Commerce.'

He grinned. 'I noticed.'

'You're avoiding the subject.'

His glance was innocent. 'What subject?'

'Chris!' she said with exasperation, although she couldn't help smiling.

'Why is it that a woman can never be satisfied until she's dissected a man's love life, put it under a microscope and examined it from all sides?'

'Because a woman knows what's really important.'

'Not fishing rights, eh?'

'No, Christopher, not fishing rights.'

He heaved a sigh. 'All right,' he began. 'Do you want to know about the French journalist in Beirut, the Spanish dancer in Mexico City or the American painter in Paris?'

His face was impassive, but a gleam in his eyes made Rachel suspicious. 'Mmmm—the American painter.'

'Let's see—she thought she was the female equivalent of Picasso and had the entire Sixties' rebellion tied up in her own person. She would have been called bohemian once; she liked to wear odd-looking clothes and peculiar make-up.'

'She doesn't sound like your type.'

'Oh? Do I have a type?'

'I'd say that you are far too conservative to go for a bohemian.'

'Conservative—that's really quite devastating, Rachel. I prefer to think of myself as dashing, gallant, handsome and charming. But conservative . . .?'

She couldn't help smiling. 'Conservative,' she said firmly.

'All right—well, I *was* too conservative. She didn't last more than a couple of months actually. She was damn sloppy, to tell the truth. And she swore all the time. My ears burned continuously.'

'And the Spanish dancer?'

'That was my exotic, Latin period. Sultry flamenco dancers wearing mantillas and clicking castanets.'

'And that lasted . . .?'

'About four weeks actually. I couldn't stand the late

hours and the smoky bars. Besides, I don't look good in sombreros.'

'And the French journalist?'

'Didn't speak English. We made love in sign language. Very interesting.'

Rachel gave him a scolding glance. 'You're making this all up, aren't you?'

'To some extent.'

'But you haven't exactly been a monk for these past ten years?'

His gaze was level. 'No.'

Ah—that hurt more than it should have. Of course, there had been women, but Rachel suddenly discovered that she didn't want to know the fine details, the drawn-in shadings. She preferred the hazy, unformed images in her mind to definite female shapes and personalities. And besides, the question she really wanted to ask was not—what are these women like? What she really wanted to know underneath was—how did they compare? Had Christopher loved them the way he'd loved her? Had their bodies moved him the way hers had? Had he stroked them with the same caresses that had driven her so wild during those long, lazy afternoons? But one doesn't ask those questions of an old lover; it's not acceptable etiquette.

'And you?' he asked. 'I can't quite see you alone for ten years.'

'There have been a couple of men,' Rachel said and wondered if he, too, were curious about those other lovers. 'They were medical students.'

Christopher was looking down at his food. 'I see.'

There was an awkward moment of silence and then Rachel said, 'Tell me about your mother.'

'There's not a lot to tell. She died very suddenly; the doctors seemed to think that she had a heart attack.'

'Were you in Ottawa when it happened?'

Christopher shook his head and picked up his wine glass. 'In Beirut. I had to fly back.'

Rachel gave him a sympathetic glance. 'That must have been hard. You were close to her, weren't you?'

Ten years ago Christopher would have shoved this question off with a glib rejoinder. He hadn't talked much about himself then. Oh, he would willingly tell her that he loved her, adored her, worshipped the ground that she walked on, but no other emotion could be discussed—not anger, fear, insecurity or anxiety. And he'd never wanted to talk about the past. His father was a *verboten* topic of conversation, and his mother was only spoken of in loving and respectful terms. Rachel had only met her once, when Christopher flew her to Washington for Christmas. It hadn't been a successful meeting. Mrs Blake had been quiet and polite, but Rachel had felt those fierce dark eyes assessing her and had known, without a shadow of doubt, that the older woman hadn't liked her.

'Yes,' he said slowly. 'Her death was hard to take. I . . . cared a lot about her, and she was devoted to me. I wouldn't be where I am today if it hadn't been for her. She wanted so much for me, and she sacrificed her life to make sure that mine would be better. I didn't see her often; I was constantly on postings, but I always knew that she was there.' He gave Rachel a small, sad smile. 'She was my own personal cheering squad. I loved her very much.'

'Yes,' Rachel said with an unconscious touch of bitterness in her voice, 'I could see that she was very proud of you.'

Christopher caught the bitterness. 'I thought you liked her.'

'No, I didn't.'

'You didn't?'

Her wine glass was empty and now she turned it round and round, watching the way the candlelight was reflected in its gleaming surface. 'You were so driven,' she said slowly, 'and so ambitious. I'd never met a man like you before who had such a need to get ahead.' She gave him a small smile. 'Maybe you're still like that, I don't know. But when we were going together, I was really only secondary to your career. I always knew that even if I didn't want to admit it to myself. But I've often wondered how much your mother was a part of it. I often thought that perhaps . . .' her voice faltered a bit, '. . . that she blinded you to everything but success.'

It was as if she had slapped him across the face. Christopher had been leaning forward to catch her words, but now he sat back, quickly, abruptly. 'She only wanted the best for me.'

'As she saw it.'

'Rachel . . .' he began warningly.

'She wanted you to be an ambassador. She set very high standards for you, didn't she?'

'I chose my career,' he said coldly.

'But don't you see, Christopher? Once you'd chosen the means, she chose the end. And I wasn't to be a part of it, was I? She didn't approve of me; she didn't want us together for fear I might push you in a different direction. There was a chance, wasn't there, that I might convince you to leave the foreign service and settle in Washington? Did she tell you to get rid of me—that I was an albatross around your neck?'

'For God's sake, Rachel. You don't know what the hell you're talking about. The fight was between us, not you and my mother. *You* didn't want to leave Washington; *you* had to finish your degree and go to medical school. I would have taken you with me when I left.'

Now, Rachel sat back, stunned. 'Oh, Christopher. You can't rewrite history. You never asked me to marry you—never.'

His attack was immediate. 'And would you have come if I asked? Would you?'

'I . . .'

'The truth now, Rachel. Don't distort the truth.'

She swallowed. 'No, I wouldn't have left Washington.'

'Well, there's your answer. Neither of us were willing to budge from our ambitions. You had to get that medical degree; you wanted to be a doctor. If you want to get personal, Rachel, we can now delve deeply into your psychological make-up and try to find out why that damned degree was so important to you. I never really believed that you went into medicine for that glorious goal of being a healer.' He waved away her immediate objection. 'Oh, I'll admit that you were an idealist and you mouthed a lot of fine notions at me, but I always thought that you wanted to become a doctor for other reasons.'

'Like what?' she demanded.

'Like filling your father's shoes. The doctor who died before he ever had a chance to cure sick people.'

Rachel couldn't take it all in. Her father—her dead father? She had never known him except as a picture in a photo album, a tall man with blond hair and an engaging smile. Rachel had asked about him when she was small; such questions as—what was my Daddy like or did he love chocolate ice cream or had he wanted a little girl? Then, as she had got older, she had stopped asking such questions, understanding how silly and babyish they were. She had known by then that Michael Sims had wanted to be a doctor himself and was just completing his residency when the accident occurred. Phyllis had always told her how pleased he would have been if he had known his daughter wanted to be a doctor, but Rachel had never connected her ambition to the father she had never known.

'It was Rob who talked me into becoming a doctor.'

'Rob just fanned the flames of something that was already there. And you always talked so much about *your mother*—how hard she was working so you could go to medical school, all the sacrifices she was making.'

'Well, she was.'

'And by becoming a doctor, you'd take over the place your father had left. You could become the provider and the support.'

'She never asked me to do that,' Rachel said heatedly.

'Do you send her money, Rachel?' She shook her head. 'No? Then I'm sure you put money aside for her—just in case. Yes, I thought so.'

'All right,' she said defensively. 'What's wrong with it? You were supporting your mother.'

'Nothing's wrong with it, but the point is that neither of us were independent ten years ago. Other people had expectations of us that we thought we had to fill. We were both young and still very tied to family. You're right about my mother; she did have high ambitions for me. But think of Phyllis and Rob, and their pride in you and the way they expected you to succeed.'

'Christopher, I wanted to be a doctor. I've always wanted to ever since I was a small child.'

'Yes,' he said impatiently, 'but you were also driven by motives that had a lot less to do with intellectual self-fulfilment than you think. Rachel, don't you see what happened to us? We were trying to satisfy everyone as well as ourselves.'

'Are you trying to tell me that it would be different now? That if we had another . . . affair, that it wouldn't end the same way? You're not about to give up your career. Look how close you are to being where you want to be. It will be Rome next, won't it? Or London? And as for me,' Rachel added vehemently, 'I have no intentions of ever giving up my practice.'

The waiter arrived, removed their plates and took their dessert orders. When he had gone Christopher leaned forward and lightly touched the back of Rachel's hand as it curved around the base of her wine glass. 'But think of the difference in honesty,' he said, 'and in our expectations. That was part of the problem, wasn't it? We thought we could have everything: our independence, our careers, the future.'

Rachel felt the warmth of his fingers on her hand, the gentle stroking. She wanted very much to turn her own hand upwards so that their palms could meet, her fingers intertwining with his in the old way. How many dinners had they shared where they'd kept their hands and fingers laced together, needing that physical contact even when they ate? Too many for her to count.

Slowly she withdrew her hand out from under his. 'I wonder what the point of all this is?' she asked coolly. 'We have our own lives now, and I don't see them coming together ever again no matter how honest we are or how sincere about our expectations. It seems to me that this dinner is a futile exercise.'

'Rachel.' His voice was seductive. 'Rachel, I . . .'

'You lied to me, didn't you? That day you came into my office.' Rachel tilted her head slightly to one side, her eyes narrowing at him. 'All that talk about researching the past—that was the real camouflage. You want to start up where we ended, go to bed with me again, have another . . .' Her beeper went off then, loud and shrill even though it was in her handbag under her seat. She almost didn't hear it, so intent was she upon the words she had to say and her growing anger.

Christopher glanced around him. 'What's that?'

Rachel took a deep breath. 'My beeper,' she said, reaching down into her bag and switching it off. 'I'll have to call my answering service.'

They both stood up then, and several other diners turned to stare at them. They were, without realising it, a handsome couple; a tall man in a dark grey suit leaning solicitously over an elegant woman, equally tall, whose hair, coiled and swept up on her head, gleamed golden under the lights of the chandelier. There was no way for the other diners to know the sudden tension between them or that, in order for them to contain it within the boundaries of a public place, their politeness to one another was now excessive and ornate, like a carefully orchestrated minuet.

'I'll have the *maitre d'* get us a 'phone,' said Christopher.

'That's not necessary,' Rachel said. 'I'm sure there's a 'phone in the foyer.'

'I'll have him get us the bill.'

'Yes.'

'Your shawl.' Christopher reached behind her and pulled the white wool shawl from the back of her chair.

'Thank you.'

By the time Rachel had reached the 'phone, she'd almost put her conversation with Christopher aside. As she dialled the number of her answering service, she felt that nervous tightening in the region of her stomach. Perhaps someday she would get used to being called out of parties, dinners or a deep sleep, tossing off the unknown crisis out there as simply part of her job, but right now she could not rid herself of the belief that when the beeper went off, it was a bad omen, a portent of injury, catastrophe or death.

'Dr Sims here,' she said.

'Sorry, Dr Sims, but you're wanted at Sibley Hospital,' a nasal voice spoke in her ear. 'A car accident involving Eleanor Foley. They're taking her into surgery, and Mrs Foley asked that you be there.'

Ellie, Rachel thought. Oh, my God, it's Ellie.

Christopher left Rachel at the Emergency Room exit and pulled into the hospital's parking lot. Their conversation in the restaurant had been all but forgotten during the car ride when Rachel, tense and pale, had answered his questions in brief monosyllables. From what he could gather, Ellie Foley was the five-year-old daughter of one of Rachel's closest friends, Samantha. She was now also Ellie's regular doctor and had been an unofficial medical adviser since birth, seeing her through teething, nappy rashes and common colds. Christopher tried to draw Rachel out further, but she wouldn't talk. It had shocked him to discover that

there were places she could go in her head that he
couldn't follow. When she had been young, she'd been
as transparent as glass, emotion and thought altering
her expression so that he'd been able to read her every
mood. Now, she was so withdrawn from him that she
barely knew he was there.

'Shall I come in?' he had asked as she opened the car
door to leave.

'What? Oh, if you want to.' And with that, she was
gone, rushing towards the hospital entrance, her wool
shawl left behind in the car, its soft yarn still holding
the scent of her perfume so that if Christopher closed
his eyes, he could almost imagine that she was still
sitting near him.

He had stared at the shawl, draped over the front
seat, its white a patch of colour in the dark, and had
decided to wait it out in the hospital. He didn't want to
interfere, but he suddenly discovered that he was
curious about her work and how it had changed her.
Rachel wasn't the same woman that he'd known ten
years ago; he'd realised that in the restaurant. She had
seen right through him, coldly and precisely. She'd
known right away that all his talk was 'camouflage'.
The old Rachel would never have been able to do that;
she'd been gullible, wide-eyed and naïve, thinking that
the world operated on some high, moral plane, and that
he and everyone else lived according to the standards
she'd set for herself.

Christopher had thought he loved her then, but he
had always known, underneath, that the chances of a
future for them were unlikely. Rachel had been right
when she said that she'd always been secondary to his
career; everything in his life had played second fiddle to
his need to succeed. His childhood had been a hard
struggle to get good grades, to help his mother, to earn
a few dollars by mowing lawns and shovelling snow and
delivering newspapers. He'd gained a scholarship to
college and had spent his six years at university waiting

on tables and keeping his nose to the grindstone. Thousands of other hopefuls across Canada had taken the foreign service exams along with Christopher, but only one hundred had been selected. Hard work, perseverance and the hot, bright flame of ambition had pulled him out of poverty and into a profession. For the first time in his life, Christopher actually had money, a nice apartment, a car, and socially he'd been catapulted into the sophisticated world of international diplomacy. That he'd lost a part of himself *en route* to such success had not really occurred to him until now—when he was thirty-five, single and feeling that in some sad way that it had been, perhaps, all wasted and useless.

But he hadn't felt that way at twenty-five. He'd been cocky then, arrogant and possessed of an overweening belief in his own intellectual superiority. He'd had a ruthless streak and stepped on toes on his way up, but the means had always seemed to justify the ends. He'd focused for so long on that climb upwards that nothing else and no one else had mattered to him. Male acquaintances were contacts; women were for sexual release. Not that Christopher wasn't a gentleman; he knew how to play by the rules that women considered important. He was kind, considerate and charming, but his emotions were only skin deep. His heart had never been engaged—until he met Rachel.

He would never forget the first time he had seen her. It had been at the Kennedy Center. Christopher's date had known Rachel's escort, and the two couples had met, by accident, in the lobby during intermission. He could no longer remember either the show he had seen that night or the face of the woman he had brought with him. All he could recall was that moment, as the introductions were being made, when Rachel turned to him and smiled. It was one of the sweetest smiles he had ever seen, sunny and warm and changing a face that, in profile, had seemed rather austere. The smile had crinkled her nose a bit and put a dimple in her left cheek. She had smiled at him with her mouth and her eyes, wide and brown between their fringe of dark lashes. The smile, total and accepting, had touched something in Christopher that had never been touched before. He had fallen for that smile first; the rest had followed—the awareness of her as an attractive woman, his enjoyment of her wit, the pleasure he took in a temperament that was even and constant and happy.

And then there was the sex. Sex like he had never known. Sex with laughter and fun, jokes and teasing. Sex in which passion and play existed side by side. His memories of Rachel were inextricably bound up with their lovemaking and the physical texture of her; hair thick and silky, a wrist so delicate he could encircle it with his thumb and middle finger, breasts small and high and pink-nippled, a gentle swell of abdomen. He'd been dazzled by her and had lost track of everything else. The Embassy became a place he had to put in hours until he could see her again, memos interrupted the pleasant tenor of his thoughts, meetings were sheer drudgery. For the first time in his life, Christopher ignored the weighty burden of his responsibilities, shucking them aside in favour of dreams and pleasure. His goals, that glittering stellar constellation of positions; high commissioner, ambassador, deputy minister, had dulled in comparison to the reality of Rachel. And then his mother had come for her Christmas visit . . .

Christopher sat up straighter behind the wheel of his car and stared out at the darkened parking lot, his dark eyebrows pulled together in a frown. During dinner, Rachel had accused his mother of stepping between them, of interfering in their relationship. He'd denied that, but now it occurred to him that he'd been wrong. That Christmas visit had marked a turning point for him, a time when he'd come down to earth from that dizzying plane of passion and sensuality. Not that his mother had ever said anything specific. That had never been her way.

'So you're happy here,' she had said one morning, sitting on the couch and knitting. She always knitted; Christopher could barely remember a time when his mother would sit down without needles and a skein of yarn. Sweater after sweater had emerged from those strong and capable hands.

'I was lucky. Washington's the best of the postings,' he'd said, sitting beside her and admiring how good she looked. Sophia Blake had aged well, considering the hardness of her life. No one looking at her would have guessed that she had slaved in other people's houses or brought up a son virtually single-handed in a home that had no indoor plumbing. She was tiny and upright, her grey hair pulled neatly back from her face into a thick bun. She had strong features, some of which she had passed on to Christopher; dark, intense eyes, eyebrows that ran straight across a wide brow, a square, stubborn chin.

'Not lucky,' she said, shaking her head firmly. 'You were the best, that's why they brought you here.'

'Now, Mother . . .'

'You've worked hard,' Sophia went on. 'They gave you that promotion.'

Christopher sipped at his coffee. 'Mmmmm.'

'And such a generous raise. They must think a lot of you.'

Christopher gave her a smile. 'It couldn't be that you're prejudiced?'

Sophia gave him a stern look. 'You're going to be very successful, Christopher. I've known it since the day you were born.'

'A mother's intuition?' he asked in a teasing voice. He liked to scold her for her blatant confidence in him, but inwardly Christopher thrived on it. He'd often been frightened as a little boy, afraid of the town that mocked him and the severity of their life. Sophia had always been behind him, encouraging him when he wavered and setting standards for him that were high but not unrealistic. The love between them was the most important relationship that he knew; his mother's pride in him the secret source of his resilience and strength. Christopher had always believed that it had been Sophia, staunch and determined, that had made him the man that he was.

'All I knew is that you wouldn't be like your father.' Sophia finished the end of one row and turned her knitting around.

'No,' Christopher said slowly. His memories of the father that had died when he was eight were brief but painful. A tall man stumbling into the house, stinking of cheap gin. A voice that slurred, skin that was always half-shaven, hands that slapped him whenever he got into reaching range. And the cruelty of other children, imitating the way Martin Blake swayed down streets and slept, like an animal, on the pavements. Even now, Christopher rarely drank; he was afraid of liquor, afraid that his father's weakness might have been hereditary.

'And that girl you've been spending so much time with. What about her?'

'Rachel?'

'She seems rather infatuated with you.'

It had been on the tip of Christopher's tongue to tell his mother all about Rachel; how wonderful she was and how happy she made him, but that urge died. 'We're very . . . fond of one another.'

Sophia had picked up a dropped stitch, her eyes lowered. 'It's nice,' she said in a seemingly placid tone, 'that you're not lonely here.'

It had been very subtle and unemotional, but Christopher, always sensitive to his mother's voice and way of thinking, had understood the unspoken message. Rachel was an intruder, a girl who'd fallen for him and who filled an empty, but essentially minor, niche in his life. It was 'nice' that he wasn't all alone but, on the other hand, he shouldn't forget what really counted; his job and his growing salary—every step that led him further and further away from the memory of his drunken father and that small Saskatchewan town where the Blakes had been the subject of shame, scorn and pity.

His mother's influence had been strong; the boy that still existed in the twenty-five-year-old Christopher had responded immediately to her words and her silent rebuke. He had begun to judge Rachel differently, to see her through his mother's eyes and to make decisions that were rational instead of emotional, pragmatic instead of idealistic. Rachel was lovely and great in bed, but she was young, inexperienced and often unsophisticated. He wasn't sure that she'd be great material for an ambassador's wife. In his daydreams, Christopher had seen himself standing next to a woman who was gracious, stylish and elegant. She would be the perfect hostess, knowing the names of all the guests and understanding the subtlety of international politics. It would also help, he had believed at that point, that she would have the sort of family and monetary connections that would speed him along his route to higher things.

Although Rachel always listened to him when he talked about his work, she wasn't fascinated by politics or trade, and she had her own dreams. Christopher started to listen to her more closely when she talked about becoming a doctor. Beneath her sweetness, he sensed a will of iron; one, perhaps, that was as strong as his. He saw no future for them and slowly he began to pull away from her, calling her less often, separating himself emotionally as best he could. By the time the actual break with Rachel came, Christopher could be cool and uninvolved; he'd brainwashed himself into believing that, not only wasn't she good marital material, but that he no longer cared for her. In that final battle, he'd held her at arm's length and watched her break down, her face crumpling before him, her voice pleading with him. He had been quite analytical about it and proud that he could be so aloof. But when she'd run off, something cold and tight inside him had snapped. Like a great wave, emotion had come roaring back into him; pain at the hurt he'd inflicted and an aching sense of loss.

Christopher had leapt to his feet and raced after her, the rain beating in his face, his voice calling above the sound of traffic, but he'd been too late to catch her and he had to go back to the restaurant and pay the bill. He'd wavered for days after that, his hand reaching towards the telephone to call her and then pulling back, his eyes turning to every tall, blonde woman that walked past him, his body restless in an empty bed. And then, when he'd got so desperate with a longing to see her that he thought he'd go mad, the long hand of External Affairs had intervened. The posting to Paris had come through along with another promotion and a pay raise that meant he could buy a place in Ottawa and let his mother live there. Pragmatism had prevailed and Christopher had not contacted Rachel again. Two months after their break-up, he had arrived in Paris, having put the past behind him and determined to forget that Rachel Sims had ever existed.

Looking back on it all, Christopher was still loath to blame his mother for what had happened. She had not been an evil woman or Machiavellian; she had not been filled with self-pity or thought to realise herself through her son's success. Sophia Blake had merely loved enough to make the sacrifices she saw as necessary so that her son would not have to live the life she had. Her ambition for him had been fierce and intense, and perhaps that had blinded her, as Rachel said, to everything in his life other than his career, but Christopher still did not see his mother as flawed. The flaw, if there was one, had been in himself. He had always let his head rule his heart and, in doing so, had ignored the heart's demands. It had shrivelled with neglect and dried up in the aridity of his soul. The women he had known since Rachel had not touched him in any emotional way; they'd become objects, delicate and lovely objects that were satisfactory to look at and, occasionally, pleasurable to take to bed.

It hadn't occurred to Christopher until this moment that the ability to love does not come easily, but requires nurturing and practice and a willing spirit. He had rather thought that one day he would turn around and find another woman the way he had found Rachel; spontaneously and unexpectedly. He had waited, so to speak, for Cupid's arrow to come slanting in his direction without any effort on his part. That it hadn't happened, he'd attributed to chance, to bad luck, to an indifferent fate. And he'd come to believe that love didn't exist, at least, not for him. But now he saw that the fault lay within him. His heart was just a husk, hollow and listless.

He had the choice of ignoring the way he was, of keeping along the path he had chosen, of looking forward to a future that was not much different than the past except that it held bigger houses, larger limousines and more elegant cocktail parties. Or he could stop the treadmill and get off, stepping down into an unknown place where the rules and rewards would be different and where his definition of success would be meaningless. The thought was dizzying; it made him feel as if he were in free-fall, hanging nowhere with vistas of space swinging around him. For the first time, Christopher realised the full implications of his mother's death. Sophia was his last link with the old life of wishes and dreams and ambitions. Now that she was gone, there was no one on this earth who really cared what he did. It was a thought that should have made him sad, but instead he felt suddenly invigorated. He was free now, free to change and free to ... love. Except that he didn't know if he wanted to change, and his heart was no longer practised in love, its beat muted and low.

'You want to go to bed with me again,' Rachel had said, accusing him of the very sin he had intended to commit.

His motives had been selfish. He had wanted to ease the pang of lust and his own loneliness with a superficial relationship. He had wanted to treat Rachel the way he had all the other women in his life, as an object to acquire for pleasure and then discard when it's no longer worth the time or effort. It was, Christopher saw now, the coward's way out, the way of a man whose heart held itself closed, insular and shuttered. It would take courage to try to love Rachel and face that same agonising choice he'd faced ten years ago. This path was dangerous, risky and inherently painful. And it would be all or nothing this time. All or nothing.

CHAPTER SIX

RACHEL wearily untied the top strings from the mask that had covered her mouth and nose for the past three hours and, letting it dangle to her chest, took in a deep breath and rubbed the back of her neck where the muscles were tight and strained. Her hair was concealed by a surgical cap and her black dress had been discarded for shapeless hospital pants and smock. The figures around her were clothed the same, their physical attributes concealed by the pale green fabric whose colour turned a sickly pastel under the white, harsh glare of the operating room lights. The room was not as full as it had been moments earlier. The small figure that had been on the table was now in the recovery room, and several of the nurses had left along with the surgeon who had another emergency case two doors down. It had been a bad night at Sibley Hospital.

The anaesthetist gave her a grim smile. 'It always seems worse when it's a child.'

Rachel nodded. 'Yes.'

'Well, she should be okay now, barring infection and complication.'

'God forbid.'

'You going to talk to the child's mother?'

'Yes,' said Rachel, 'she's a close friend.'

He gave her a sympathetic pat on the arm and was then gone. Rachel took one more look around the operating room and sighed when she thought of Ellie's tiny face, pale and waxen against the white of the sheets. She'd had a mild concussion, several cracked ribs and a broken tibia, none of which was as serious as the ruptured spleen which had caused vast quantities of internal bleeding. Well, she was fixed now, but it would

be weeks, maybe months, before she'd be the Ellie that
Rachel had known; active, energetic and spritely, a little
girl with brown pigtails that stuck out like wire brushes
and freckles sprinkled beneath eyes that were as blue as
the sky.

And Samantha was going to find it difficult to deal
with a full-time job and a full-time invalid on her
hands, Rachel thought as she pushed open the doors
and stepped out into the hallway, brushing past a
rushing nurse and an orderly pushing an elderly woman
in a wheelchair. A voice blared nasally over the PA
system. 'Dr Atkins, Dr Filbright, Dr Moore. Your
presence is requested in emergency services.' And the
sound of it reminded Rachel of her residency, of
sleeping on a cot in a small office, of being awakened by
such a voice time and time again, of getting only two or
three hours sleep after two or three days of non-stop
work. Residency; a time when she'd lost twenty pounds
and discovered that she could fall asleep anywhere.
Rachel's weariness hit her again, a profound and deep
exhaustion that came from the stress that surgery had
always placed on her and compounded by the fact that
she had a deep affection for that tiny sleeping figure
whose body had been handled, marked, cut into and
sewn up. She felt drained and empty and would have
given anything to simply lie down on any horizontal
surface and go to sleep, but there was still work to be
done.

When she'd arrived at the hospital, she'd found
Samantha pacing the corridor in front of the nurses'
station. She was a pitiful looking figure and almost
unrecognisable; her prettiness gone and her vivacity
replaced by an almost insurmountable anxiety. She had
a bandage at her temple, a bruise that was swelling on
her jaw and the skin below one eye was already
violently discoloured. Her trousers and blouse were
torn and stained, and someone, a nurse probably, had
taken pity on her and draped a hospital jacket over her

shoulders. She couldn't sit still and was walking back and forth, crying softly and wringing her hands.

'Oh, Sam,' Rachel had said, putting her arms around her.

Samantha took one look at her sleekly coiled hair and black cocktail dress and started crying. 'You were on a date,' she said. 'I've ruined your date.'

'Don't be silly. It doesn't matter.'

'I'm so . . . sorry.'

'Sam, don't apologise.'

'It's just that Ellie—she's hurt . . . badly. I know it. Oh, God,' she sobbed, 'what have I done?'

Rachel had put her arm around Samantha, led her to a chair in the waiting room and, praying it was true, mouthed the platitude, 'I'm sure she's going to be all right. Preston is operating and he's one of the best.'

It's funny how well platitudes work in emergencies. As Rachel had expected, her words gave Samantha hope. She sat up and sniffed. 'You think so?'

Firmly. 'Yes, I do. Now, I'm going to go into the operating room and you're to sit here and wait for me. The minute I can give you any news, I will.'

She'd started to move away, but then Samantha had pulled at her hand. 'Rachel, it's all my fault.'

'What is?'

'Ellie's being hurt. It's my fault.'

Despite her eagerness to get to Ellie, Rachel saw that she was going to have to deal with Samantha first. 'You mean the accident?'

'I was wearing a seatbelt,' Samantha said slowly and the tears once again came into her eyes, 'but I . . . I didn't put a seatbelt on Ellie.'

Rachel sat down next to her. 'Tell me exactly what happened,' she said soothingly.

The facts were told between sobs and were slightly incoherent, but Rachel didn't have any problem sorting out the sequence of events. Samantha had been driving back from an evening with friends, and Ellie, cranky and whiny at that late hour, had insisted on lying down in the back seat. So Samantha had obliged her and had not insisted that Ellie put on one of the seatbelts which were awkward to attach when the child was prone. It had been, after all, only a ten-minute ride home. Samantha had automatically buckled on her own seatbelt and had, therefore, escaped major injuries when a car had ploughed into them from a side street. It was Ellie who'd been tossed around like a bag of potatoes, crashing against the front seat and then the door and, finally, being thrown on to the pavement.

'So you see—it's my fault. I hurt her. I . . .'

There was a hint of hysteria in Samantha's voice, and Rachel assumed her most calming voice. 'Sam, you didn't know there would be an accident.'

'But . . .'

'Of course, you should have insisted that she wear a seatbelt, but you didn't and blaming yourself now is useless. Ellie doesn't need that. She's going to need love and support and a lot of patience. And she's not going to get it if her mother is crippled with guilt.' Rachel knew that Samantha would never forgive herself—never, but she also knew the right words, the right phrases that would ease some of the pain. Ten years of medical training and an unusual sensitivity had given her that skill. 'Now, I'm going to have one of the nurses get you a coffee. And you're to stay right here until I come back.'

Samantha had taken a deep, shaky breath. 'You sure learned how to be bossy in medical school,' she said.

Rachel had smiled, glad to see Samantha's sense of humour reviving. 'Right,' she'd said. 'We took a course in it—How To Order Patients and Their Relatives Around.'

'I believe it,' Samantha'd said mournfully.

The waiting room was empty but for two figures when Rachel got there. It was a plain, sterile place, but then most hospital waiting rooms were like that—bland, colourless walls, chairs that looked like motel furniture, illumination that brought out the worst in a person's face instead of the best. Sometimes music was piped in over the public address system, but fortunately, they were spared that tonight. It was close to two o'clock in the morning and, by hospital standards, the building was relatively quiet.

The two figures were huddled together on a double seat with their backs to Rachel. She had, at first, thought they were strangers, but then she saw that one of the heads, the one with curly brown hair, belonged to Samantha. As she rounded the corner of the couch, she realised with a sudden surprise, that the other head, the hair dark and slightly tousled, belonged to Christopher. She'd forgotten all about him; about their dinner, the conversation, the drive to the hospital and his asking if he could stay and wait for her. Rachel supposed she'd agreed, although she couldn't actually remember doing that.

Samantha and Christopher were asleep, his cheek resting against her head as she leaned against him. He'd taken off his jacket and rolled up his sleeves, and his bare forearm, muscled and sprinkled with dark hair, curled around Samantha's shoulders. They both looked exhausted. The lines in Christopher's face that ran from mouth to nose were etched deeply, and he was pale under the lights. Samantha's good eye, the one without the bruise beneath it, was darkly circled. For a second, Rachel was loath to wake them. They seemed so peaceful sitting there in a moment of stolen comfort and, besides, a lump had risen in her throat, a reaction to this evidence of Christopher's kindness. Samantha had needed someone during the long hours of this night, and silently Rachel thanked Christopher for being there.

Finally, she sat down next to Samantha and gently touched the other woman's arm. 'Sam,' she said.

Samantha's eyes flew open and, struggling out from under Christopher's arm, she leaned forward, fear on her face. 'Rachel, how is . . .? Is she . . .?'

'She's fine.' Rachel was aware now that Christopher was awake and staring at her as if he didn't know who she was. She took one of Samantha's clenched hands between hers. 'She had a mild concussion, some cracked ribs, a broken left tibia, assorted cuts and bruises and a ruptured spleen. Her head and ribs will heal themselves and we set the leg. The worst problem was the spleen; it was causing a lot of internal bleeding. Preston decided to remove it.'

Samantha swallowed. 'The spleen? What does it do?'

'A number of things. It filters out foreign bodies that infect the blood stream, it destroys old red blood cells and it creates white blood cells, but,' she added calmly, 'other parts of the body can do the same thing so its loss isn't vital.'

'Oh.' Samantha didn't say anything after that, as if she had to take the information and slowly process it so she could understand it better. But Rachel knew that she was feeling better, her fist was unclenching, her fingers slackening against Rachel's palm.

Christopher cleared his throat. 'Where is she now?'

'In the recovery room. She's still sleeping, the anaesthetic hasn't worn off yet. I think, Sam, that they might let you go in and see her now if you want.'

Samantha stood up quickly and then rocked back and forth as tiredness and dizziness struck her. Both Christopher and Rachel were beside her immediately, each with a hand under her arm. Samantha gave them both a wan smile. 'Sorry about that,' she said.

'No problem,' Christopher said and added tongue-in-cheek, 'as long as you quit drinking.'

'It must have been that last martini,' Samantha said.

'The one with the olive.'

'Yeah—the olive. That's what did it.'

Rachel smiled to herself, liking the fact that

Samantha still had some of her old spirit left and appreciating the way Christopher had instinctively known how to handle her.

'Christopher heard my life story,' Samantha said to Rachel as they started to walk out of the waiting room, 'including our high school love life.'

'*Our* high school love life?'

'Now, what were their names again?' Christopher said, winking at Rachel. 'Bud and Joe, Jim and Eric.'

'Not Eric,' Rachel said with a groan. 'God, Sam, you really dragged out the dirty linen.'

Samantha gave a helpless shrug. 'He insisted—he's a persistent sort.'

Christopher and Rachel exchanged a glance over Samantha's head. His eyes were amused, hers held a wary acknowledgment. 'Yes,' Rachel murmured. 'He certainly is.'

Rachel slept on the car ride to her apartment, and Christopher had to shift slightly in his seat to accommodate her weight as she leaned against his shoulder. He knew that she hadn't wanted to fall asleep; she sat over on her side of the front seat, talking about the surgery and staring straight ahead. But her words had been garbled and, the next thing he knew, she had slumped down, her body sliding over until her head rested against him. Gingerly, he put an arm around her and pulled her closer to him, liking the feel of her close to him, her arm bare beneath his hand, tendrils of her hair curling against the lapel of his jacket.

It was now after three in the morning, and Christopher could see why she was dead on her feet. Samantha had spent about fifteen minutes with Ellie who was still asleep and likely to be that way until the morning. She had wanted to stay at the hospital all night, but the arguments of Rachel and two of the recovery room nurses had prevailed. Ellie wasn't going to heal any better with Samantha sitting by her bedside, she needed a decent's night sleep which she'd get better in her own bed, they'd 'phone her the moment Ellie awoke. Samantha had reluctantly agreed, and Christopher and Rachel had taken her home, a drive of forty minutes to a northern Virginia suburb. Even he was tired, and he hadn't been in surgery for three hours.

It had been quite a shock for Christopher to see Rachel in her hospital clothes. At first he'd hardly recognised her. She'd looked like someone on television—an actress dressed up as a doctor. But then she'd sat down next to Ellie and started talking, and Christopher had realised just how competent and professional Rachel really was. He'd understood then that he'd never quite taken her career seriously. Oh, he knew the trials and rigours of becoming a physician in the abstract, but Rachel had accomplished her training in his absence, and he had no real idea what those years of schooling had entailed. And seeing her in an office setting had not brought home to him the reality of her work. What had made him fully comprehend what she did was the rumpled hospital clothes, the hair caught severely back in its cap, the quiet way she had talked to Samantha, that aura of knowledge and ability.

Rachel dealt with life, its beginning and its endings. She'd held babies, minutes old in her hands, and had sat at the beds of the dying. Her work was important and vital and necessary, and it humbled Christopher to realise it. He thought about the Embassy with its crisis-a-minute atmosphere that was nurtured on the statements of politicians, the machinations of bureaucrats and the manoeuvrings of government. He and the other diplomats acted as high-level reporters and skilled negotiators. Much of what he did seemed important at the time, but next to the kind of work that Rachel did his own seemed grandiose, overblown and pompous.

For the first time since he had joined the foreign service, it occurred to Christopher that, as Minister, he was involved in a gigantic game which thrived on the need of certain segments of mankind to prove their dubious value. He thought of the ridiculous protocol problems and of dignitaries who must be addressed by the proper names and seated in the proper rank. Then there was the tangled red tape of every bureaucracy he'd ever dealt with including his own. Just recently, he'd been caught in the cross-fire of memos on a subject so petty as a request for a coffee machine. And finally there were all the high-flown sentiments and patriotic statements that hid the gritty and dirty reality of politics. Compared to the practice of medicine, the practice of diplomacy seemed to him to be artificial and lacking in dignity.

It was his first seed of doubt about the values and importance of his career, and it was being planted in a fertile field, but Christopher didn't see it that way. He berated himself for losing his perspective on life and, brushing off his thoughts as he pulled over to the kerb beside Rachel's apartment building, he switched off the car's engine.

'Rachel,' he said. 'We're here.'

She was sound asleep, her breathing even and steady, her body relaxed against his. Although the car was dark, a street lamp shed illumination into the front seat, its light catching in the honey-blonde strands of her hair. Idly, Christopher picked up a tendril that had strayed over his shoulder and wound it around his finger. It was soft and silky and gleaming, and it brought back memories of making love to Rachel, of having her over him, her head bent forward, her hair falling on to his bare chest, his neck, his face. Without thinking about what he was doing, Christopher moved his hand on to Rachel's head and dug his fingers into her hair, feeling the curve of her scalp beneath his palm and then the delicate nape of her neck.

Rachel gave a soft sigh and moved closer to him.

'Hey,' Christopher said. 'Wake up.'

'Mmmm?'

'Rise and shine.'

'Shine?' she mumbled.

'All right—no need to shine. But I don't think you want to sleep in the car all night.'

Rachel took a deep breath and pulled herself upright, blinking. 'How long have I been asleep?'

'Since we dropped Samantha off.'

'I don't think I've ever been so tired.' She rubbed her eyes as if the friction would rouse her. 'What time is it?'

'Around three-thirty.'

'Oh.' It was a moan of misery. 'I have to be up at five-thirty.'

'Five-thirty!'

'Hospital rounds begin at six-forty-five.'

'Come on then,' Christopher said. 'Let's get you home.'

Christopher thought that the apartment guard showed great restraint when they entered the building. He merely glanced at them for a moment and then looked away. It was an act of kindness, because when Christopher caught sight of Rachel and his own image in the mirror on the foyer wall, he winced. They were the picture of debauchery. His tie was loosened and his suit jacket was rumpled. There were circles under his eyes, his hair looked as if it hadn't been combed in weeks and his cheeks were dark with growing beard. Rachel looked even worse, if that were possible. The sleek chignon had been destroyed by the surgical cap, and her hair fell in disordered tangles on her neck and around her face. Her make-up was either non-existent or smeared, and her elegant black dress with its straight skirt, brief bodice and narrow straps looked as if she'd been in and out of it more than once. Which was precisely what had happened, Christopher thought with a wry irony. In her hurry to get into the operating room clothes, she'd obviously neglected to hang the dress up. Its skirt was creased beyond redemption, the zipper up the back was not quite up and one strap kept slipping off her naked shoulder. To put it in the most unflattering terms, the two of them looked like hell.

Rachel was like a zombie all the way up in the lift to her apartment. She stood leaning against one wall and staring vacantly at the lift doors. When they opened, she stumbled slightly, catching the high heel of her shoe in the carpet. Christopher caught her arm. 'Easy,' he said.

'I'm sorry,' she said.

'Sorry about what?'

She gave him a tired smile. 'For being such a klutz.'

'I'm not too co-ordinated at this time of the morning either.'

They were walking down the corridor, but now Rachel stopped and stared at him. 'You know,' she said in a clinical voice, 'you look terrible.'

He pulled her along. 'You always were handy with a compliment.'

'No, seriously, Chris. I think you should get a good night's sleep and take tomorrow off work. You need the rest.'

'And what about you?'

Rachel yawned as they reached her door. 'I'm used to it.'

'To what?' Christopher asked, leaning against the doorjamb and watching her dig through her handbag for her key.

'To not getting any sleep. It's an occupational hazard. Besides I have appointments set up all day. Lots of sick kids.' She yawned again and opened her purse wider. 'Why do keys always do this to me?'

'Here, let me look.'

The keys were lying right on top of her wallet, but he didn't say anything.

'Now,' Rachel went on, 'insert one brass key into appropriate keyhole.' But her hand shook slightly, and she couldn't make the connection.

Christopher took the keys from her hand without comment, opened the lock and swung open the door.

Rachel's smile was sweet and slightly unreal. 'Christopher, that was so clever of you,' she said, flicking on the foyer light.

He closed the door behind him. 'That's what they all say.'

As Rachel put her shawl in the hall cupboard, Christopher looked around him. Her apartment was attractive, the living room long and narrow with a bay window at one end. Two couches formed one conversation area; occasional chairs marked another. It was a serene room, and Christopher found that he liked its mix of wicker and upholstered furniture, of plants and paintings, of greys and blues and whites. Rachel's taste had been unformed when he'd met her first. She'd been only twenty and very unsure of herself. She had always craved his approval, asking for it until he gave it and then doubting it so that he was forced to give it again. But maturity had obviously changed her. There was no uncertainty in the way she'd juxtaposed styles, colours and patterns together or in the room's quiet harmony.

'Nice apartment,' he said.

She didn't blush either now or look surprised. Rachel had, Christopher discovered, developed a considerable dignity. 'Thanks,' was all she said.

Christopher wearily ran a hand through his hair. 'Well, I guess I'd better head . . .'

But Rachel had kicked off her high heels and was now walking towards the bathroom, pulling the pins out of her hair and letting the blonde curls fall to her shoulders. 'There's coffee in the kitchen,' she said. 'You should drink some before driving home.'

'It's only a twenty-minute drive.'

Rachel shrugged. 'It's up to you.'

'Well . . .'

She gave a huge yawn. 'And don't worry about the front door when you leave. It locks automatically.' She was about to close the bathroom door when she paused.

She turned slightly so that she was facing him fully again and said, 'By the way, I didn't say thanks.'

'Thanks for what?'

'For helping Samantha.'

It was Christopher's turn to shrug. 'It was a pleasure.'

For a second, it seemed that Rachel was about to say something, but then she seemed to change her mind. She yawned again and said, 'Good night, then.'

'Good night.' Christopher watched her go, the door shutting behind her. So that's how it was to be. Casual and friendly. As if they were a pair of old acquaintances. Help yourself to coffee and then let yourself out. Don't mind me and I won't mind you. The tensions that had arisen over dinner had dissipated through the long and arduous night. Well, it made sense. They were both tired; they both had to get up and work in a few hours. There was no point in continuing a conversation that required adrenalin and energy. Not that he intended to quit. He was finding that he liked the new Rachel even more than he'd liked the old one. Or perhaps, he had never liked the old one. Not really. That had been infatuation compounded by youthful lust—a fatal mixture.

Smiling to himself, Christopher wandered into the kitchen. It was a place that looked rarely used, the rust formica counter perfectly clean, the stainless steel gleaming in the overhead light. By the toaster was a canister of granola cereal, a jar of raisins and a bag of dried apricots. Hanging over the back of a stool was a dish towel with a black chicken on it that read 'Black chickens lay white eggs.' Christopher contemplated that surrealistic thought for a moment and then opened a few of the cabinet doors until he found a jar of instant coffee. He took it in his hand, gazed at it and put it back on the shelf, muttering to himself, 'The hell with that.'

He didn't want a coffee, he didn't want to drive home

and he didn't want to go to bed alone. As this desire came to him, Christopher shifted restlessly, knowing how absurd it was even to contemplate such a possibility. Rachel would never permit him to stay the night. He had no rights, he was nothing more than a tired ex-lover who was feeling lonely. But the idea was seductive, and he couldn't stop himself from leaving the kitchen and going into Rachel's bedroom. It was a soft, feminine place, decorated in lavenders and mauves, scented from Rachel's perfume. A lamp by the bed cast an intimate, golden glow over ruffled pillow slips and the tufted bedspread. An incredible weariness came over him at the sight of that bed. He thought he could lay down on it and sink into its comfort, the warmth of Rachel's body against his own, the closeness of her flesh easing his own into a deep and dreamless sleep. His reluctance to go back to the emptiness of his large and elegantly appointed house grew stronger and more persuasive. What would be the harm? he asked himself. He didn't have any urge to make love to Rachel, he was far too tired for that. And they'd slept in the same bed so many times that there was nothing shocking in doing it again—one more time.

Christopher glanced at the bed and felt the tug of it draining him of the little bit of energy that he had left. His body ached to lay horizontal, his head yearned for the softness of a pillow, every muscle clamoured for stillness and peace. Would Rachel object? There was a very strong chance that she'd be outraged but, on the other hand, there was a slim possibility that she'd be amused. With the sort of reckless gambling spirit that comes with extreme fatigue, Christopher decided to go for broke. He stripped quickly, placing his shoes beneath a chair and his suit neatly draped over it. He was nude then, a tall, lean man with muscled legs and a broad chest. Silently he slipped between the cool sheets, the mattress yielding underneath him. The scent of Rachel's perfume was even stronger now that he was in her bed, his head lying on her pillow. He stretched, luxuriating in the freedom from clothes and the heavenly sensation of being prone.

God, but he was tired. He hadn't been this tired in months, and it was the exhaustion that comes of mental stress rather than physical effort. Samantha had been a bundle of nerves when he'd found her. It hadn't been hard to guess who she was. There were only the two of them in that particular waiting room and, when he'd asked if she was Ellie's mother, she'd practically fallen on his shoulder in sobbing gratitude. The three hours of surgery had seemed endless. He'd let her talk about any subject that came into her head and didn't question her when her conversation was confused or incoherent. Finally, she'd leaned against him and slept and Christopher, to his astonishment, had dozed off as well. He didn't think he'd ever fallen asleep sitting upright in his life.

And now he was in Rachel's bed. It was odd how things worked out, he thought, and it was even more peculiar when he considered how his position would look to an outside observer. No one would believe that his motives were innocent; his intentions pure. His lying nude in Rachel's bed had all the makings of a seduction scene. In his fatigue, his mind worked like a camera making lazy, unfocused shots. A Lady's Boudoir. The Bed. A Close Up On The Hopeful Seducer. And His Ignorant Victim? Where was she? Taking a bath from the sounds of it, Christopher decided, and then he fell asleep, still smiling at the images in his head, his eyes shutting, their dark lashes sweeping down against his cheekbones, his body falling endlessly into that black void.

Rachel's lower back ached almost unbearably. She had thought just to wash her face, brush her teeth and fall into bed, but the pain in her back was so excruciating that she hadn't thought she'd be able to fall asleep.

She'd drawn herself the hottest bath possible and was now soaking in it, her body slowly turning pink from the heat of the water and her muscles loosening. She closed her eyes and let her head fall back against the bath pillow. Ah, that felt so good, she thought and then smiled. She was becoming so relaxed, she was in danger of falling asleep and drowning under ten inches of water.

Surgery always had this effect on her. She was usually tense throughout an operation, and the fact that tonight's patient was someone she cared about hadn't helped her level of tension. Add to that the dinner with Christopher, and the sum was hours of adrenalin pumping through her system. When it had finally drained out of her, sometime during the drive back to her apartment, Rachel had been close to collapse. Her head had ached, her hands had trembled and her back had felt as if a knife was being turned in its muscles. What had happened, she wondered, to that medical student who'd been able to live through one crisis after another in a permanently numb state? That earlier Rachel could fall asleep at the drop of a hat and wake up an hour later, bright-eyed and bushy-tailed. Well, she thought ruefully, perhaps this Rachel was getting too old for that. Or perhaps it was Christopher. That conversation at dinner had certainly taken its toll.

Idly she wondered if he'd had his coffee and gone. She supposed so; she wouldn't have heard the door close over the sound of water filling the bath, but she didn't hear any sounds now. Rachel knew she hadn't been the perfect hostess when they arrived, but she didn't think that Christopher minded and, at that point, she couldn't have cared less. All she had wanted to do then was wash her face and rid herself of the pins that held up her hair. Their pressure on her scalp drove her wild after a while, a state of affairs that was aggravated by the surgical cap. And then there was her back and the enticement of the bathtub and ... well, it didn't matter. She was sure that Christopher would understand.

He'd changed. He was more ... Rachel sought for the right word ... compassionate. Yes, that was it. He was more sensitive and sympathetic. She couldn't see the Christopher of ten years ago holding a stranger's hand for three hours. The younger Christopher had been in such a hurry to go places, to accomplish what he wanted to do, to forge the success he wanted to achieve. He hadn't had time for other people. The fact was he'd barely had time for her. She hadn't realised that then. She had thought he'd been doing the right thing by working late at the Embassy and bringing a briefcase full of papers home on the weekends. She'd awoken many mornings to find the place next to her empty and had known that Christopher was working in his den and wouldn't want to be disturbed for hours. She'd never complained, but then she'd been so ... grateful. Rachel grimaced at the word. Yes, that's what she'd been, utterly and ecstatically grateful that someone as marvellous as Christopher wanted her. Their affair had seemed so wonderful to her that she hadn't been able to believe it when he'd turned cooler and had started to distance himself from her.

Rachel felt the old hurt start up again and resolutely ignored it. Leaning forward, she pulled the bathplug and stood up, pulling a towel off the nearby rack. The mirror over the vanity unit was cloudy and reflected only a misty image of pinks and golds back at her. She stepped out of the tub and made a small circle in the mirror with the corner of the towel. Her face looked back at her and she winced. She looked awful. Well, at least her back didn't hurt anymore. And she wasn't going to agonise over Christopher and the past. It was over and done with, wasn't it? A closed chapter, terminus, *finito*.

Rachel towelled herself dry and, after hanging the towel over the shower rack, stepped out into her bedroom. She was naked, her body was a golden colour, smooth and gleaming, her nipples a dark-pink in the shadowed room, the triangle of hair below her stomach a deep honey-blonde. Lazily she raised her arms above her head in a long, reaching motion, luxuriating in the feeling of every muscle stretching and then, as she took a deep breath, lowering her arms. To bed, she thought. Even a couple of hours of sleep would help, although she'd still be a disaster tomorrow. Well, Molly would step in; she was terrific that way. She often knew when Rachel was tired and would buffer her against any additional pressure and . . .

Rachel froze, her mouth wide in an O of astonishment, her eyes blinking at the sight of Christopher asleep in her bed. *Christopher in bed.* For a second, she had an odd sensation of *déjà vu*—as if she'd been transported back ten years to other scenes of Christopher in bed. Then Rachel gave herself a mental shake. What the hell was he doing there? Had he thought he could use her apartment, her bed? Had she even given him the slightest hint that he could stay the night? Rachel quickly ran the events and words of the last half hour through her mind and decided, no, absolutely not, she'd not said a thing, there hadn't even been an intimation that . . .

And it was obvious that he was completely naked. The sheet over him had slipped down to a point just below his waist, its hem resting lightly on the muscled tautness of his abdomen. He was lying on his back, one arm flung up over his head, the other resting across his chest, his fingers splayed across the dark triangle of chest hair. He was, Rachel saw, dead to the world. He hadn't heard her come in; he hadn't heard the bathroom door open and close. There were still lines of fatigue etched deeply on his face, but he was at peace, lying there against the ruffled pink and mauve of her pillow, his hair curling on his forehead in boyish waves.

Rachel knew that she should be furious that

Christopher had the audacity to think he could stay the night and to sleep in her bed without even asking. No one would blame her if she marched over to that bed, shook him violently awake and told him, in no uncertain terms, to get lost. She could then point out the obvious—that he had no right to be there, that the status of old lover didn't entitle him to any extra privileges or benefits. But, the trouble was that Rachel wasn't angry; she couldn't even drum up the proper sense of outrage at Christopher's flagrant flouting of the conventions. She was not only far too tired for that but, underneath, she was also amused. Rachel couldn't help it; she liked the unexpected, and nothing could have been more unexpected than finding a naked Christopher in her bed at—she glanced at the luminous dial of the clock on her bedside table—four o'clock in the morning. Four o'clock! Inwardly she groaned.

There was always the bed in her den, which was also the guest room. She could dig out some sheets and blankets and sleep there. That seemed feasible for less than the space of a second. Rachel tried to imagine herself having the energy to open out the sofa and make the bed. Her imagination failed, and she bowed to the inevitable. Sighing softly, she walked over to the bedside-table and switched off the lamp, throwing the room into dusky shadows, already lit by the pale light of the rising summer sun. The sheets were cool on her side and the mattress barely moved as she slipped in next to him. As her legs moved down into the bed, her toes brushed against him and, for a second, she let her foot rest against his leg. It felt good, she thought sleepily, to have a man's body next to her in bed again. She liked the solidity of Christopher, the warmth and the steady sound of his breathing. She turned on her side then and he turned in the same direction so that her body curved around his. Rachel snuggled closer, put her arm around him so that her hand was against his chest. Then, taking a deep breath, she fell asleep.

CHAPTER SEVEN

RACHEL awoke from the depths of a deep sleep, not to the shrill and clamouring sound of her old Baby Ben alarm, but to the soothing touch of hands gently kneading her lower back. It was a wonderful feeling, and she lay quite still, her eyes closed, her body easing under those knowing fingers. They massaged muscles that had become stiff again and loosened the tightened joints in her spine. And the palms were so warm. She could have stayed in that position forever, luxuriating in sensation, feeling pampered and taken care of. 'Mmmm,' she murmured, starting to doze off again under the ministrations of those wonderful hands, and then remembered Ellie and Christopher and the hospital rounds this morning. Her eyes blinked open and she made a sudden motion upwards, bringing a sickening jolt to her stomach and a groan to her half-opened lips.

'Easy.' The warm hands gently pushed her back towards the bed.

Rachel felt terrible: her eyes were gritty and her head ached. The last thing on earth she wanted to do was crawl out of her warm bed and away from those hands, but she had to. Her work called; the hospital called, she had to go and check on Ellie. 'But I have to get up. I have to . . .'

'It's not five-thirty yet.'

Rachel sank thankfully back into the bed. 'It isn't?'

'Uh—uh.' The fingers began working over her muscles again.

The bedroom was light but shadowed by the curtains which blocked the windows. 'What time is it?'

'A little after five.'

'You mean— you woke before the alarm?'

'I can do that. Set my own internal alarm.'

Rachel closed her eyes, and the aching in her head dissipated. 'I'd forgotten about that,' she said. Christopher had never needed any help getting up in the morning. He'd had that uncanny ability to wake himself at a certain time no matter how many hours he had slept. She gave a deep sigh and added, 'That feels so good.'

'I thought it might.'

Rachel gave a small shudder of pleasure as his fingers walked up her spine. 'How did you know my back hurt?'

'You kept rubbing your back last night.'

'I did?'

'You don't remember?'

'I don't remember much after leaving the hospital.'

'Well, you slept in the car, staggered into your apartment and took a bath.'

'Oh, yeah. I remember that.'

'And then . . .' His voice took on a dramatic note.

'And then?'

Christopher heaved a heavy sigh. 'I guess you went to bed.'

Rachel smiled to herself. 'No, I didn't rape you while you were sleeping.'

'Damn.'

'In fact, I considered kicking you out.'

'But then you took pity on my helpless state.'

'No. I took pity on myself. I was too tired to kick you out.'

'You sure know how to hurt a guy's ego.'

Rachel yawned. 'And I was too tired to make up the bed in the other room.'

'And you couldn't resist the lure of my naked body.'

'And I was too tired to give a damn,' she said and then couldn't help a small purring sound as the fingers dug into a particularly tired spot between her shoulder blades.

The fingers lifted. 'Too tired to give a damn, eh? Continue in that vein, my lovely, and this salubrious digital friction on your epidermis will terminate forthwith.'

'Salubrious digital friction?' Rachel asked in disbelief.

'Healthy massage, by any other name.'

Rachel rolled over and stared up at Christopher. He was lying on his side, one elbow bent, his hand propping up his head. The other hand, the one that had been massaging her back, now cupped her bare shoulder, the thumb making soft circles against her skin. They were both naked above the waist, but it didn't seem to make much difference. Christopher had seen her many times that way.

He was smiling down at her, but the smile couldn't erase the marks of fatigue on his face. The grey eyes were bloodshot, and there were dark circles above his cheekbones. His hair was in chaos and his beard was coming in, its blackness giving him a villainous look.

'You look terrible,' she said conversationally.

His grin widened. 'You, too.' Rachel's hand went automatically to her hair. 'But not from the neck down.' His eyes moved to her breasts. 'That part looks pretty good.'

'Really,' Rachel said.

'Well,' Christopher said, giving her an assessing look. 'The contours seem to have withstood the ravages of time. Mind you, they're not quite as ... perky as they were ten years ago, but then you're not twenty any more and ...'

'Christopher!' Rachel sat up and pulled the sheet up over her breasts, her tiredness receding as she glared at him. 'You really have a lot of nerve. You know that, don't you?'

'Mmmm—I had a feeling you might think that.'

'I didn't give you any hint that you could sleep here.'

'No, you didn't.'

'And nothing I ever said implied that I might be the slightest bit interested in a physical relationship.'

'No.'

'In fact,' and Rachel moved her hand sharply to emphasise the point, 'I thought I made it perfectly clear that I didn't want to sleep with you.'

'Yes, you did.'

'But you stayed anyway,' she said accusingly.

'It looks that way.'

'It doesn't *look* that way—it *is* that way.'

Christopher's grin disappeared, and in its place was a slight twist of the lips, not rueful exactly, but giving him a vulnerable look. 'Rachel, I want to . . . to make love with you.'

'I *knew* it! I just knew that's what you wanted. All the *rest* of it, the *dinner*, the polite *conversation,* the *talking* about the past. That was all phoney, wasn't it? A whole lot of . . .'

Christopher caught the hand that she was waving wildly in the air. He held it gently in his own hand and then lifted it to his lips. His kiss was warm and soft against her palm, and Rachel inadvertently shivered.

'I'm sorry,' he said. 'I was being dishonest.'

'You've always been dishonest.'

'No,' he said automatically and then stopped. 'Yes, maybe you're right.'

'You were dishonest about us before.'

'I've thought about what you said at dinner and, yes, my ambitions overshadowed everything in my life.'

'Including me.'

'Including you, and my mother *was* a factor.'

'You see, I told . . .'

Christopher gently interrupted her. 'But not the deciding one. She influenced me, but I was ready to be influenced. And I didn't feel strongly enough about you to fight her assumption that you were secondary to my career. I was . . . too self-centred, too selfish, too obsessed with myself. Rachel, I didn't deserve you.'

There was a short silence in that bedroom where the summer sun fought to make its way through the curtains and ripples of shadow and light coloured the bedspread, the sheets, the faces of Rachel and Christopher. They were staring at one another, Christopher's admission hanging between them, precariously hanging on the uncertainty of their feelings towards one another. There was a vulnerability to both of them, and it was compounded by their fatigue, by their nakedness, by the intimacy of being next to one another in a bed once again. The air hung heavy with unspoken emotions and revelations.

Rachel pulled her hand out of his. 'And what makes you think you deserve me now?'

'I don't know it I do.'

'But you want to try.'

Christopher ran his fingers through his hair, tangling the dark strands even more. 'I'm a different person than I was,' he finally said. 'I'm not sure what I expect out of a relationship with you, but, yes, I do want to try.'

The old irritation surfaced. 'But, Christopher, nothing's *changed*. I have my work here and you're on a rotational posting. It will all come to the *same* thing again.'

'Maybe not.'

Rachel sat back against the pillow and stared at him. 'What do you mean—maybe not?'

'The future's not ordained.'

'I have no intentions of ever giving up my practice.'

'I know that.'

'Are you saying that you'd give up the foreign service?' Rachel asked with incredulity.

Christopher sighed and shook his head. 'I don't know what I'm saying—except that I refuse to believe that life is so arranged in advance that I should make decisions based on something that may or may not happen four years from now.'

Rachel lifted her chin. 'So you want to have an affair—open-ended, so to speak.'

'We've both changed, and I want to explore a relationship with you.'

Rachel wrinkled her nose. 'That sounds like a cover-up for sex.'

'I already told you. I want to make love to you.'

'Yes,' said Rachel in a bemused tone, 'you already told me.'

'And you want to make love to me.'

Her eyes widened. 'I do?'

'Yes.'

'Aren't you taking an awful lot for granted?' she asked heatedly. 'Aren't you . . .?'

His forefinger rested against her lips, stopping the flow of outraged words. 'Rachel, I believe you want me as much as I want you. If I didn't think that I never would have taken you out to dinner or stayed here last night.'

'I wouldn't sleep with you now!'

'No, not now.' Christopher glanced at the clock. 'It's almost five-thirty, you have to get up and I'm not in any condition to overwhelm you with my masculine charms. This isn't the right moment.'

She was still angry. 'Maybe there isn't any right moment.'

'Maybe there isn't,' he conceded, 'but think about it, will you?'

Rachel watched as Christopher slipped out from the sheets and stood in the shadowed bedroom, his body still as long and as lean as she remembered, the back broad, the buttocks firm, the legs heavily muscled in the thighs. He was a handsome man, well-made and very sexy. Of course, she wanted to go to bed with him; that, she acknowledged readily. But wanting and doing were two different things. Wanting meant that she could remain a slightly frustrated spinster with an absorbing career and little time for emotional crises. Doing implied a different lifestyle altogether. Resuming an affair with Christopher would put a strain on her that hadn't existed before. Oh, the sexual aspect of it would be wonderful, and it would be very pleasing to have masculine companionship again, but their times together would always be tainted with the knowledge of his eventual departure from Washington. Rachel didn't take Christopher's talk about leaving the foreign service very seriously. When an ambassadorship beckoned, she knew he would go.

Christopher picked up his clothes from the chair and his shoes from beneath it. Then he turned towards her. 'I'm just going to use the bathroom,' he said. 'I won't take very long.'

'That's all right,' she said.

'And I'll let myself out.'

'There's coffee in the . . .'

'No thanks. I'll get some at home.'

There was an awkward pause and then, 'Chris . . .?'

'Yes?'

'Thanks for the . . . ah, salubrious digital friction.'

He grinned. 'No charge.'

'I mean, I would have felt terrible without it.'

'That's okay—you can pay me back sometime. I like massages, too.'

Rachel swallowed. 'There may not be a "sometime".'

The room was too shadowed for their eyes to meet or their expressions to be really visible to one another. Rachel couldn't really know the impact of her words on Christopher. She couldn't see the sudden stiffening of his body or the slight downward turn of his mouth. All she could hear was his voice which sounded relaxed and nonchalant.

'It's up to you,' he said.

'I . . .'

'I won't be calling you, Rachel. You'll have to get in touch with me.'

And then he was gone, the bedroom door shutting behind him.

*   *   *

Rachel met Samantha by Ellie's bed. The hospital outdid itself when it came to the children's ward. There were colourful pictures on the walls and stuffed animals on every surface. Mobiles of stars and moons or farmyard animals dangled over the beds, and some artist had painted the window at the end of the hall in great geometric patterns of red, green and blue so that it seemed as if the sunlight were coming through stained glass.

Ellie's bed held all her favourite toys behind its metallic bars, a Cabbage Patch kid with bright red braids, a Winnie-the-Pooh bear, a dozen picture books and a beloved blanket, pink and worn almost to threads.

Samantha held it up when she saw Rachel. 'I was washing this at five o'clock this morning,' she said. 'It's original condition was disgusting.'

Rachel smiled and looked down at Ellie who was sleeping. The child looked frail, her eyelids traced with the delicate blue of veins, her skin a pasty white. Her brown hair lay in wisps on the pillow. She had a tube in her nose and a bruise that was blossoming on one temple. The rest of her was covered with a thin blanket, but Rachel could see the bulky outline of the bandages that covered the abdominal incision the surgeon had made the night before.

Rachel glanced at the chart at the end of the bed. 'She's doing fine. No fever, no post-op crises.'

'I know. The nurses told me.'

Rachel now took a good look at Samantha. 'Did you get any sleep?' she asked in concern, noting the deepened purple shadows under her eyes. Samantha had changed to a fresh pair of slacks and blouse and had obviously made an attempt to pull a comb through her brown curls, but she still looked worn and bruised.

The other woman grimaced. 'I tried. How about you?'

'About an hour.'

Samantha gave her a tired smile. 'You look better than I do, Dr Sims.'

'A hot shower will work miracles,' Rachel said. 'Look, I'm almost finished with my hospital rounds. When I'm done I'll come back with some coffee.'

Samantha sighed. 'That sounds wonderful.'

Rachel's final rounds consisted of stopping at the bed of one little girl who was recovering from pneumonia and a baby who'd had major surgery for an intestinal blockage that was as rare as it was unexpected. The baby was, not surprisingly, making great gains. Children healed so quickly, Rachel thought, as she picked him up and felt the weight of him wiggle in her arms.

'Oh, no, you don't,' she said as he reached for her earring, his brown eyes bright with curiosity and mischief, his round face intent.

'He's a terror,' one of the nurses said. 'Grabs everything.'

'And eating well, too,' Rachel said, feeling the heft of him. 'He should be going home tomorrow.'

'And not too soon. We've got another cold making the rounds.'

Rachel shook her head in commiseration, thinking that hospitals were sometimes dangerous for one's health. The children's ward was a breeding ground for respiratory ailments. It didn't seem to matter what illness a child entered with, when it left it would have a runny nose. Short of putting each small patient in isolation, there wasn't much they could do. She was still pondering that thought as she picked up two coffees in the restaurant on the basement level and took them back up to the third floor. When she got to Ellie's bedside, she found Samantha leaning back in the chair, her head against the wall, her eyes closed. But she opened them as soon as she heard Rachel's footsteps.

'That smells good,' she said as she accepted the styrofoam cup, a spiral of steam rising from the surface of the coffee.

'Are you going to stay here all day?'

'I thought so. I want to be here when she wakes up.'

'Mmmm.' Rachel took a sip of her coffee and glanced at Ellie who hadn't budged since she left. 'Has she been awake at all?'

'The nurse said she woke up and cried at about four, but then went back to sleep.'

'Well, they've got her on painkillers and that will keep her drowsy.'

'Yes.'

For a moment, there was a short silence as they both drank their coffee, and then Samantha said carefully, 'I thought Christopher was wonderful.'

Rachel was equally as cautious. 'He was, wasn't he?'

'We were strangers, but he sat with me all that time while I blabbed and cried, blabbed and cried.'

'That *was* kind of him.'

'You know,' Samantha said, 'I sort of pictured him as the devil with horns on his head, cloven hoofs and a forked tail.'

Rachel couldn't help smiling. 'Well, he did seem like the devil at the time.'

'I thought you weren't going to see him again.'

'It's hard to explain, but he did call and he was so persistent and then he showed up at my office with a borrowed baby and . . .'

'A borrowed baby!?'

Rachel gave a helpless shrug, her shoulders lifting the white hospital coat. 'I know, it was absolutely ridiculous, but there he was with a baby on his knee, saying he knew that was the only way I'd see him.'

Samantha smiled. 'You have to give him credit for ingenuity.'

'Well, I did and went out to dinner with him.'

'And Ellie and I came along to interrupt your tête-à-tête.'

Rachel shook her head. 'It wasn't quite like that. In fact, I think we were arguing when my beeper went off.'

'And then what happened?'

'We came here and you know the rest.'

'Oh, no,' Samantha said with a knowing look. 'You can't pull the wool over my eyes. What happened after that?'

'What did you do?' Rachel asked incredulously. 'Hire a detective?'

Samantha looked smug. 'Call it intuition.'

'Well, then your intuition will tell you.'

'Good try, Rachel, but it won't work. Let's see. Christopher stayed the night.' Rachel didn't answer but sipped at her coffee so Samantha went on. 'He slept in your bed, took you into his arms and made wild, passionate love to you.'

'Wrong and you have a dirty mind, as always.'

'Ah-ha, that clinches it. He stayed the night but you didn't make wild, passionate love.'

Rachel gave her an exasperated look. 'How did you know?'

Samantha put one hand in the air and tilted it from side to side. 'Something in the tone of your voice. It always gives you away. You couldn't lie to save your soul.'

'All right, he did stay the night. He wasn't invited, but he crashed on my bed.'

'And . . .?'

'He wants to have an affair.'

'See—I told you.'

'Sam, you did not. You said we made wild, passionate love.'

'If you didn't actually do it, you were thinking about it. So what did you say?'

'I said that nothing's changed.'

'And he said. . .?'

'He said that we've both changed and he didn't deserve me before.'

'Now, that's romantic.'

'No, it isn't. He's fishing and I'm the bait.'

'How do you know he's not sincere?'

'I don't know,' Rachel said wearily. 'I don't know what to think.'

'Now let's look at the pros and cons,' Samantha said and Rachel, watching her, gave an inward smile. Samantha loved to dissect people and relationships; the subject of an affair just perked her up no end. And Rachel was willing to talk about her sex life with Christopher until kingdom come, if it kept Samantha's mind off Ellie for even a few seconds.

'Okay,' she said.

'Pros first.' Samantha lifted one hand and counted on her fingers. 'One, Christopher is handsome and eligible. Two, he's kind and generous. Three, he wants you back. Four, you need a man in your life and he'd fill the bill.'

'Who said I need a man in my life? Sam, that's chauvinist.'

But Samantha ignored her and lifted her other hand. 'Now, the cons. One, you're both carrying emotional baggage around from ten years ago. Two, you're both being so damn pragmatic that the whole thing sounds a bit like a trade negotiation instead of a love affair. Three, Christopher is still in the foreign service and you're a doctor.'

'There,' Rachel said, 'number three, that's the crux of it.'

'We can discard the earlier emotional baggage?'

'I think so. I'm not ... angry at him the way I was.'

'Hmmm. And what about the pragmatism? It doesn't sound like you're being swept off your feet.'

'Should I be?'

'Well,' said Samantha musingly, 'it is rather nice to enter into a love affair thinking that you're in love.'

Rachel glanced down at her hands which were cupping her coffee. 'I don't think either of us is in love with the other.'

'You're sure about that?'

Rachel looked back at Samantha and then slowly shook her head. 'I'm not sure about anything.'

'All right,' Samantha said briskly. 'Let's just say that sex is the overriding factor.'

'But . . .'

'Well, it is, isn't it?'

'Sam, you make it sound so . . . so,' Rachel couldn't find the right word so she settled for 'physical.'

Samantha gave Rachel a shrewd glance. 'You do want to go to bed with him, don't you?'

'Can I plead the Fifth?'

Samantha gave her a grin, her first truly enthusiastic smile since Ellie's accident. 'You can plead anything you want, honey chile. It doesn't mean a thing.'

'Well, there you are—that leaves the issue of our careers.'

'What difference do your careers make?'

Rachel gave Samantha a surprised glance. 'What difference? You know the answer to that.'

'Look around you, Rachel, and you'll see dozens of relationships that didn't survive even though they were undertaken with every intention of being permanent. Life doesn't guarantee happy endings even if you're anticipating the fact that you're going to be the exception to the rule. *I* got married thinking it was forever and see where it got me.'

'But starting off with Chris and knowing that it will end isn't the same thing.'

'True, and it will certainly give your affair a bittersweet feeling, but you might have some wonderful years and, when it's over, lovely memories. You know what I have from my years of marriage—nothing but bitterness and the memories of one fight after the other.'

'But . . .'

Rachel was interrupted by the arrival of a nurse who was carrying an enormous white box wrapped with an equally enormous red ribbon. 'This just arrived for

Ellie,' she said, handing it to Samantha. 'Special delivery.'

Samantha gave Rachel a quizzical shrug. 'It's big enough,' she said wryly.

Rachel glanced at her watch. 'Who could have sent her a gift so quickly? It's only eight-thirty. The stores aren't open yet.'

But Samantha had opened the small card at the top of the box and now gave a small cry of delight. 'What a nice man,' she said.

Rachel craned forward to look at the card. 'Who's it from?'

'Harvey.'

'Harvey Campbell?' she asked in disbelief.

'We were there last night.'

'At Harvey's house?'

'He's divorced and has a daughter Ellie's age, Suzanne. She lives with the mother, but was visiting for the week. We were there for dinner and Ellie fell in love with this doll that Suzanne had. I'll bet that's what's inside.'

'How did Harvey know that . . .?'

'I called him this morning.'

'I see.'

Samantha finally turned her attention back to Rachel and gave her a shamed look. 'I didn't tell you about Harvey, did I?'

'No, Sam,' Rachel said with severity, 'you didn't.'

'Well . . . we liked one another when we met at that lunch and he would call me to chat and we went to a movie one night and then he invited me to dinner.'

'How serious is this?'

'Not serious yet.'

'But?'

'Well, it might head in that direction. I know Harvey isn't the world's most gorgeous male specimen, but he makes me laugh and God knows, I need it. You see, Rachel, I'm not asking for a future that's all wrapped up and handed to me with a big red bow,' and Samantha's hand unconsciously ran over the package on her lap. 'I'm willing to take any happiness that comes my way, even if it's only going to be short-lived.'

Rachel could understand Samantha's logic, and it was very persuasive. Take what you can where you find it, and the hell with the consequences. That kind of philosophy even had a name—hedonism, and there were any number of people who ascribed to it. The trouble was that Rachel wasn't sure she was one of them.

'But, Sam,' she said, her voice low, 'what if I fall in love with Christopher all over again?'

Samantha glanced at the sleeping form of her daughter and, reaching her hand through the metal bars on the bed, caressed Ellie's pale cheek. 'It's always risky,' she said slowly, 'to love anyone.'

Oddly enough, the only true hedonist that Rachel knew when it came to male-female relationships didn't agree with Samantha at all. She was having lunch with Rob in their usual place, an elegant restaurant on Wisconsin Avenue. The lunch was a monthly institution that Rob had initiated when Rachel had graduated from medical school. He always made quite a fuss about it, calling the *maitre d*' and making a reservation and then 'phoning Rachel to make sure that she hadn't forgotten. Rachel always brought a good dress with her to the office, because she knew that Rob liked nothing better than to be dining with a well-dressed woman. And he always looked as if he'd stepped out of a bandbox, his shoes gleaming, every hair in place, his suit impeccably cut and pressed. And he always arrived with flowers.

'Rob, you're such a romantic,' Rachel said as she glanced down at the half-dozen magnificent salmon-coloured roses by her plate and smelled their heavy, luxuriant scent. They were sitting at the table they always had. It was by a large curved window and looked out towards the looming grandeur of the National Cathedral.

'Nonsense,' Rob said briskly, opening his white linen napkin with a flourish. 'Living well is the best revenge—that's my motto.'

'Of course, it wouldn't suit everyone.'

'No—take your mother, for example.'

'My mother?'

But the waiter had arrived and was taking their order. It took some time because Rob was very choosy. He wanted to know what was fresh that day and what was the chef's speciality; if he was ordering meat, he wanted it done just so; and choosing the wine was a job unto itself. It wasn't until he was satisfied and the waiter had been properly instructed that Rob returned to the subject of Phyllis.

'Deciding to live out nowhere from nowhere in a cramped little cottage.'

'She likes it.'

'Hmmmph. No doubt it's mouldy, too.'

'Oh, I don't think so. Mother wouldn't live in a place that was mouldy.'

'It's the sea air, Rachel. Everything will be damp.'

'I think she's quite happy.'

'That's what I mean,' Rob said, pouncing on her words, and then grumbled, 'crazy woman.'

Rachel's eyebrows lifted, but the waiter had arrived with the wine. Rob, of course, had to follow the proper procedure. He checked that it was chilled sufficiently and allowed the waiter to uncork it. Then, a small amount was poured into his goblet. Rob lifted the goblet, stared into the ruby depths of the wine, sniffed it, sipped it and then pronounced it adequate. Rachel, meanwhile, had decided that it would be safer to veer the conversation away from her mother. Rob, of the dapper clothes, neatly groomed salt-and-pepper hair, and many women, was clearly unhappy that Phyllis had left Washington. The idea invited further investigation, but Rachel knew that Rob wouldn't admit to anything in her presence.

'Try the wine,' Rob was saying.

Rachel obediently lifted her goblet and sipped at it. 'Very nice,' she said.

He frowned. 'I'm not as happy with it as I could be.'

Rachel leaned forward. 'Rob, I need some advice.'

Rob loved to give advice. He leaned back in his seat and beamed at Rachel, the subject of Phyllis and wine forgotten. 'Financial, medical or emotional?'

'Emotional.'

'Ah,' he said with satisfaction, 'you've come to the right place. Just unburden your heart to Uncle Rob.'

'Well, it's about Christopher.'

'Christopher—are you referring to "The Christopher"?'

Rachel nodded.

'You've seen him since the cocktail party?'

'Yes.'

Rob's blue eyes narrowed. 'What about him?'

Rachel cleared her throat. 'He wants to ... to get back together again.'

'I see. And do you?'

'I don't know. I'm gathering advice on the subject.'

Their salads arrived, and Rob picked up his fork. 'Off-hand, my dear, I'd say, don't get involved.'

'But, Rob, you keep saying that I should have more fun.'

'But would it be fun? That's the issue. He made you miserable before.'

'I'm older now,' Rachel said. 'I'm smarter.'

'Hmmmph.'

'Well, I am.'

Rob picked up a heart of palm with his fork and waved it at her. 'It wouldn't be a permament relationship, would it?'

Rachel shook her head. 'We're both involved with our careers. But he is going to be here for a while. He's on a four-year posting. I could have a wonderful four years.'

'And when it was over?'

'Walk away from it.'

'And then fall to pieces and leave it to your friends and relatives to put you back together again.'

'Rob, now let's be honest, you've had a number of affairs and no one's had to go around and pick up the pieces when they're over.'

Rob put down his fork and gave her a severe look. 'Rachel, my dear, I am perfectly willing to be honest. I'm constitutionally unable to withstand a long-term relationship. I do not get emotional and distraught. I keep things at a pleasant, but very light, level. I walk away with my nerve endings intact.'

'There,' said Rachel. 'It's not so hard then.'

'That's for me,' he said forcibly. 'But we're not talking about me. We're talking about you.' This time, the tines of his fork were pointed directly at her heart. 'You don't have that protective shell. You will get yourself involved over your head. You cannot separate the physical from the emotional.'

'Ten years ago, I was immature and naïve,' Rachel protested. 'This time, I'd be going into it with my eyes open.'

Rob put down his fork again and leaned forward. There was no mistaking the seriousness of his intent. 'My dear, I've known you since you were knee high to a grasshopper. Perhaps I know you better than you know yourself. Now, I'm not presuming to interfere in your life, but in my heart of hearts, I think an affair with Christopher would be a disaster. You asked me for my advice and this is it.' And he leaned even further over the table to give a dramatic intensity to the words to come. 'Don't do it, Rachel. Please, for everyone's sake, don't do it.'

One for, one against, Rachel thought that night. She

had come home from the office, changed into jogging clothes and gone for a short run. She didn't jog regularly, but occasionally she felt the need for it. Tonight had been one of those nights. Then she'd come back, had a shower and was now sitting before the television in her bathrobe and sipping at a tall glass of iced tea. Presumably she was supposed to be watching a movie, but she couldn't concentrate. Christopher had walked out of her apartment a week ago, but she felt his presence as if he were hovering beside her. It's up to you, he had said, and Rachel had been wrestling with the decision ever since. She felt quite helpless at times as she wavered before it, a flame flickering this way and that before a strong and capricious wind.

Indecision wasn't one of her characteristics, and Rachel hated being in a state of not knowing what to do. She wanted to come to a quick choice and be done with it, but it simply wasn't that easy. She longed to be with Christopher again; she wanted to sleep with him, laugh with him, wake up in the morning and find him beside her. In her imagination, she could literally feel the sensation of his body against hers, and her dreams were filled with erotic happenings; with bodies meeting, legs tangling, lips touching. She woke up from those dreams feeling as if she should dash into a cold shower.

On the other hand, she didn't want to have his leaving hanging over her head like the sword of Damocles. Bittersweet, Samantha, had said, summing up the possible future in one succinct word. That's what an affair with Christopher would be. Bittersweet. Bitter and sweet. Happy and sad. Wonderful and terrible. Rachel didn't know if she had it in her to handle those conflicting emotions. Certainly, Rob didn't think so, and it was true—he'd known her since the day she was born. And she couldn't help wondering if the past would be repeated in the future. Would Christopher start pulling away from her again when his career beckoned? Unconsciously she sighed deeply and then suddenly felt the urge to talk to her mother, to hear that calm voice and to allow Phyllis's serenity to wash over her once again.

The 'phone rang for a long time before Phyllis picked it up.

'Mom?' Rachel asked. 'Did I call at a bad time?'

'No, I was just outside admiring the moon and stars. You know, you really can't see the night sky in Washington. Too much pollution.'

Just the sound of Phyllis's voice made Rachel feel better. 'How's your painting going?'

'Nicely. I'm working on a picture of the dunes. The colours are all beiges and browns and oranges.'

Rachel could imagine it; the scrubby brush, the sand piles high and white, the reeds waving before the wind. She could also picture Phyllis's cottage, a weatherbeaten grey structure perched on stilts. Rachel knew why her mother liked living near the ocean. There was a soothing quality to the steady sound of the waves and the flowing colours and shapes of the beach, water and sky. 'You're not lonely, Mom?'

'Rachel, I could be lonely in a crowd. I've always felt that way. No, I love it here. Isolation suits me.' She gave a short laugh. 'It must be my age.'

'How about mouldy?'

'What?'

'Mouldy.' Rachel laughed. 'Rob is sure your house is mouldy.'

Phyllis made an outraged sound, and Rachel could just see her, standing at the 'phone, glaring down at the receiver, one hand firmly on her hip, her elbow jutting into the air. 'There isn't a speck of mould in this cottage.'

'I think your absence is making him grouchy.'

'Really? Well,' Phyllis said briskly, 'he can come down for a visit.'

'He misses you, Mom.'

'Are you matchmaking, Rachel?'

'I've often wondered about you two.'

'You *haven't*.'

'Yes, I have. Rob used to spend more time at our house than he did at his own. And I don't think it was for the pleasure of *my* company.'

'I can't imagine where you ever got the idea that Rob and I were anything more than friends.'

'He's very attractive.'

'Rachel, you sound like a salesgirl with a piece of leftover merchandise.'

'But, Mom, all those years and . . .'

'Rob is a bachelor who needs to dip occasionally into domesticity to keep his feet on the ground. We're friends, that's all.'

And, Rachel thought with an inward smile, the lady certainly doth protest more than one might have anticipated. 'Well,' she said nonchalantly, 'don't be surprised if he's changed his mind.'

'This,' Phyllis said with a crisp tone, 'is a ridiculous conversation. Surely, you didn't 'phone long-distance to speculate about Rob.'

Rachel sobered immediately. 'Actually . . . well . . . I . . .'

'What is it?' Phyllis asked quickly. 'Are you all right?'

'It's . . . it's Christopher.'

There was dead silence at the other end of the 'phone and then, 'Christopher? Christopher from the Embassy?'

'Yes.'

'He's back?'

'He's posted to Washington as Minister, and he . . . wants to see me again.'

Phyllis wasn't like Rob. If she didn't like the idea of Rachel seeing Christopher again, she didn't let on. There was a long pause and then she said, 'How does that make you feel?'

'We still have our careers, but . . .' Phyllis was silent so Rachel went on, the words rushing out of her as if she were confessing, 'Well, I'm very attracted to him. I always have been.'

'Yes.'

Rachel caught the hesitation. 'You never liked him, did you?'

'It wasn't a matter of liking. It was . . . well, I always thought he was a father substitute.'

'A father substitute!'

'Rachel, you had no father and you were so trusting and so . . . needing of shelter. That's an awkward way of putting it, but Christopher had such a strong personality that he . . . well, took you over.'

'He wasn't *fatherly*. Far from it.'

'No, but he had strong ideas about what you should do and how you should act. If you don't mind the metaphor, you slipped under the wing of his personality and felt safe.'

'But I wasn't safe.'

'No, of course not. That's my point. He wasn't your father, and he had his own problems to deal with. When they interfered with his feelings for you, he discarded the relationship.'

'We were both young.'

'And now you're older.'

'Yes,' Rachel said, 'and I *don't* need a father.'

'No, I think you've grown up. But whatever you do, take care.' Phyllis's voice was gentle but emphatic. 'Watch out for yourself. And Rachel?'

'Yes.'

'Be strong.'

CHAPTER EIGHT

CHRISTOPHER sat by the pool and sweltered. It had rained earlier that morning, one of those heavy tropical rains where the clouds seem to part and the water falls in sheets. Then the sun had come out, its heat raising the moisture level in the air to an almost unbearable degree. It was good for the plants, you could almost see them growing, but it left him feeling listless and uncomfortable. He could have stayed in the house where the air-conditioning kept the temperature down, but being enclosed in four walls had made him extremely restless. The result was that he alternated between swimming in the cool water of the pool and then, even in the shade, baking on a *chaise longue*. And when he wasn't feeling too miserable, he tried to read a report about the NATO alliance and US–Canadian relations. It was slow going.

Two weeks had passed since Christopher had walked out of Rachel's bedroom. Two long, excruciating weeks that had seen his temper disintegrate, his composure fall apart and his sleep become seemingly non-existent. He had imagined in every possible configuration, the ways in which Rachel would contact him. He'd envisioned her arrival on his doorstep, her 'phone call, her letter. He'd even, at one point, optimistically informed his staff that they must, on no account, turn away a blonde-haired woman named Rachel Sims. He had, mentally, enacted out conversations, arguments, rebuttals and debates. He had seen her as loving, passionate, aloof and uninterested. He'd reacted with anger, ecstasy, coldness and fury. There wasn't an eventuality that Christopher's imagination had left untouched in that past two weeks. There had been times when he felt like a walking soap opera.

So this is what a man can come to, he thought wryly as he stared unseeing at a chapter on missile defence. It seemed a miracle to him that he had managed to retain a small modicum of humour. In fact, he rather suspected that it was all that was holding him together. In his roughest moments, Christopher had been able to stand outside himself and even feel pity for his own misery. He wondered why he was so obsessed with Rachel. There were so many women that it seemed ridiculous for him to focus on just this one. She was beautiful, yes, but there were others more beautiful. She was smart and sophisticated and poised, but any number of women had those characteristics. In fact, he'd spent one night contemplating all the women in his acquaintance that could easily step into Rachel's shoes and had come up with twenty. Twenty! But the hell of it was, he didn't want any of them.

Which left him sitting out by his pool on a hot Saturday afternoon, feeling damned sorry for himself. Christopher shook his head in disgust, put down the report and, for the fifth time that day, dived into the pool, thanking his lucky stars that the Canadian government had, for once, stepped back from a posture of penny-pinching economy and bought a house for its Minister that had a gracious, tree-filled backyard with a cabana and a large kidney-shaped pool. The water was cool to his hot skin, and he ploughed through it in a steady arm-over-arm rhythm. Having grown up in the prairies where the largest body of water to be found was in the family bathtub, Christopher hadn't learned to swim until he was in his twenties. His crawl was, therefore, utilitarian and not particularly graceful. But it got him places and forced him to expend a vast quantity of energy that left him feeling pleasantly drained. And it almost allowed him to stop thinking. Almost but not quite.

He was coming to the unhappy realisation that he had failed with Rachel. He had thought it would take her a while to decide, but the longer it took, the more likely it seemed that she would turn him down. In a way, he couldn't blame her. All the charm and good intentions in the world couldn't erase what would probably happen to them. Christopher had been completely honest when he'd told Rachel that he didn't like to think of the future as fixed. He'd grown tired of long-range plans and the vision he'd had of himself for so many years. He'd wanted to think of the future as unwritten, as unexpected, as surprising. That didn't mean that he actually saw himself out of the foreign service—that would have been far too radical—but it did mean that he wanted to enjoy the present without constantly thinking of the future. He wanted to be free, untrammelled and allowed to roam any path that he cared to take.

Christopher approached one end of the pool, turned and took off again, the water rushing past his body, his hands digging deep into its blue depths. Well, he could understand Rachel's reluctance to share that attitude. It didn't suit everyone. And it wouldn't surprise him if Rachel didn't trust him. His actions in the past didn't inspire loyalty or devotion. The truth was he'd been a bastard ten years ago. A fool and a bastard, but he hadn't known that then. He'd been so busy saving his own damned skin that he hadn't really understood what he'd done to her. Well, he was ten years older now and ten years wiser and ten years more compassionate. But why should Rachel believe that? As far as she was concerned, he might not have changed at all. And, if she didn't agree to see him again, there was no way she'd ever find out either.

Christopher cursed, his mouth half under water, and the curse emerged into the air as hundreds of small bubbles. Then he kicked harder and pulled deeper, trying to think of anything and anyone but Rachel. Of his work at the Embassy, slower because of the summer. Of the two-week holiday he planned on the

Chesapeake Bay. Of the other women he knew. Lucy Solvano, for instance. She always gave him that slow, come-hither smile. But when he tried to imagine Lucy in his arms, she changed into Rachel, golden-haired and brown-eyed. *Goddam.* Christopher raced across the pool, a tall figure slipping through the water at a furious and powerful pace, oblivious now to everything around him except the feel of his own arms and legs and a despair that threatened to drown him in its own intense depths.

Rachel arrived at the door to Christopher's house and stared up at it. The house was, by most people's standards, a mansion; brick covered with ivy, a turret in one corner, stained glass on each side of the door. It was a large building and imposing on its acre of manicured grounds. A circular driveway led up to it, and a carpet of green lawn spread out in front of it. There was a brass lion's head on the door with a ring in its mouth, and Rachel tentatively raised her hand to use it, discovered her fingers were trembling and gave herself a slight shake. What, in God's name, was she afraid of? Firmly, she raised the ring and knocked with it, hearing the sound of it echo through the house.

But her heart was thumping hard when the door opened, only to have it slow down when she saw that the person who had answered the bell wasn't Christopher. She'd forgotten that the second-in-command at the Embassy had full-time servants. The butler was short, round and officious.

'Yes, Ma'am?'

'I'd like to see Mr Blake. Is he in?'

'Your name?'

'Rachel Sims.'

'Oh, yes, Miss Sims. He said you would be coming.'

'He did?'

'Yes, Miss Sims. Come in, please.'

Had Christopher been so confident of her arrival that

he'd actually told his butler that she would be coming?
Rachel was trying to decide whether she felt insulted by
that or not as the butler ushered her into a cool foyer
with black-and-white tiles and a mahogany breakfront
against one wall.

'Mr Blake is in the pool, Miss Sims. Would you like
to wait for him here or go down?'

'I'd like to go down.'

'This way, please.'

A wide hallway carpeted in white led out into a large
living room with a grand piano in one corner and
several groupings of sofas and chairs. Above the
fireplace mantel was a large Inuit painting of birds in
colourful flight. It was the only vivid object in the
room. The rest of the décor was very soft and subdued,
and she wondered if it reflected Christopher's taste. She
suspected it didn't, remembering that the building was
owned, and probably furnished, by the goverment.

The butler indicated the double glass doors at the end
of the room, and she stepped through them on to a
terrace that overlooked the grounds at the back of the
house. Down a flight of stone steps was a cabana and
beyond that a pool. A man was pulling himself out of
that pool, hoisting himself up with his arms and then
standing on the tiles, reaching for a towel. His body
gleamed from the water, droplets running down a
bronzed chest to the muscular concavity of his stomach.
His hips were enclosed in dark-blue briefs, his legs lean
and covered with dark hair. He flung back his hair,
rubbed his chest with the towel and then ran it between
his legs. That motion made Rachel's mouth go dry.

She stood frozen to the cement floor of the terrace,
staring helplessly at Christopher, unable to move. She
hadn't known that morning what her decision would
be. She'd awoken in the same state she'd been in for the
past fourteen mornings: wondering, doubting and
wavering. It had finally come to her that she had to talk
to Christopher again. She had to explain to him why

she was afraid, why she was hesitant, why she couldn't make up her mind. Perhaps, as it was said in diplomatic circles, all they needed was another round of negotiations before reaching the final agreement—whatever that would be.

So she'd done her hospital rounds, come home for some lunch and then dressed very carefully. She'd put on a red sundress, cool and crisp, and flat white leather sandals. She'd pulled her hair away from her face and into a curled knot at the back of her head. Tiny pearl earrings marked each ear, and her eyes were made up to make them look wider, browner, softer. It had seemed important that she look her best for this meeting, even though she was well aware that, by not 'phoning ahead, there was every chance that Christopher wouldn't be home. Part of Rachel had rather hoped this would be the case. That way the decision would be taken out of her hands by fate. If Christopher wasn't home, she'd told herself, then she wouldn't be seeing him again. It was, of course, the coward's way out, and Rachel was ashemed of it, but she couldn't help herself.

But she hadn't missed him at all. In fact, he was only several yards away, close enough for her to see the individual muscles of his body and the tangled, wet strands of his hair. Rachel discovered that she was trembling, and she clutched her handbag to her chest in a vain attempt to stop the mad beating of her heart. He was drying his face now, oblivious to her, and then rubbing the towel over his hair. It wasn't until he was finished and had put the towel over the edge of the *chaise longue*, that he lifted his head and saw her standing there. For one second, he too seemed frozen, a statue, a gleaming dark Adonis. And then he was running towards her, taking the steps two at a time.

'Rachel!'

She was tight in his arms, her cheek pressed against the naked warmth of his shoulder, and she was crying and saying his name over and over again, her lips moving against his skin, 'Chris . . . Chris . . . Chris.' His face was nuzzled against her hair, his voice murmuring indistinct words. And his hands didn't stop moving. One tangled in her hair, brushing the strands at the temple and unpinning the carefully tied knot at the back so that the weight of it fell and he could run his fingers through it. The other hand ran up and down her back, feeling her and touching her as if he could never have enough of her. They stood that way for a long time, and finally he pulled his head back and looked down at her, the grey eyes blazing. 'Rachel,' he said, 'you came.'

Of course, it may have been from swimming; that would be the most logical thing. After all, he had just come out of the water. On the other hand, he had also dried himself with a towel. But perhaps it wasn't the pool water at all. Perhaps something else had dampened his eyes and turned his lashes wet and spiky. Rachel couldn't be sure, but her heart moved within her, and she knew, beyond the shadow of a doubt, that she had loved him all along.

'Yes,' she said. 'I have.'

'You haven't forgotten,' he said later.

'You neither,' she agreed lazily.

'Mmmm, of course, there are other tests.'

'Really.'

'Athletic ability, acrobatic skills. They all require testing.'

'Do they?'

'But I might let you rest for a few minutes.'

'You're so kind.'

And then later. 'Tell me, doctor, can a man die from an overdose of sex?'

'Yes. It's a classic condition.'

'Is that right?'

'Well known. Easily diagnosed.'

'Is it curable?'

'Well, it's one of those strange diseases . . .'

'Yes?'

'Where the more you engage in the dangerous activity, the more likely it is that you'll survive.'

A pause. 'I see.'

And much later.

'Chris! Oh, my God, the butler!'

'Finnigan?'

'I don't care what his name is! What's he going to think? We've been here for hours.'

'Finnigan's job is to "butle"—or whatever the hell it is that butlers do.'

'But won't he suspect . . .?'

'I'm sure he has a very good idea what we're up to.'

'I'm getting up. I can't stand the idea of him wandering around the house. I'll bet he passed by your bedroom door a dozen times.'

'No, he hasn't.'

'How do you know?'

'Darling, he gets off at six. He went home hours ago.'

'What time is it?'

'Hold on a sec while I find my watch . . . nine-thirty.'

'Oh, Chris. We've been . . . making love for five hours.'

'Mmmm—wonderful, isn't it?'

Rachel stayed with Christopher on Saturday night and all day Sunday. After that, they decided that they'd be together on weekends and not see one another during the week, but that arrangement didn't last for long. One month after Rachel had found Christopher swimming in the pool, she closed up her apartment and moved into the Minister's mansion. Her arguments against it had been feeble, his for it had been overwhelming and persuasive. But by then Rachel was no longer surprised at what she was doing. From the moment Christopher had taken her in his arms, she'd been lost: lost to pragmatism, to future considerations, to the world around her. She was, quite simply, madly in love.

It was, for both Christopher and Rachel, an enchanted summer. The diplomatic cocktail circuit was in abeyance until the autumn, and the evenings were their own. They jogged together, played tennis, went hiking and had numerous impromptu barbecues. They spent a wonderful two weeks in a cottage on the Chesapeake Bay; swimming, boating and crabbing. Christopher developed a deeper tan, and Rachel got her usual sunburn which blistered and peeled before developing into anything more refined. She came back from the Chesapeake with freckles on her nose and her skin the colour of honey. They made love often—on Christopher's bed, beneath the Inuit painting, in virtually every room in the house and, at nights, in the pool when they went skinny-dipping.

They laughed a great deal, finding the world both foolish and crazy. They had some serious conversations but these were rare. Neither Christopher nor Rachel wanted to face 'Life'—they simply wanted to live and love with exuberance. They rarely argued and only talked about what they would do that day or that coming week. They did nothing that would give either of them the slightest bit of pain, and they carefully avoided looking ahead to the future—a dark, unlit place where obstacles and unhappiness littered the pathways. It was much safer to wake up each morning, look out into Christopher's sunny garden and make plans for a day or evening of pleasure. 'Let's do the Smithsonian art museums today,' Christopher might say. Or Rachel would suggest that they pack a picnic lunch and go sightseeing in Mount Vernon.

Only once was there any mention of the future on which they had so deliberately turned their backs. They'd rented a small sailboat during their two weeks on the Bay, and the wind had died down, leaving them with nothing to do but swim off the boat and sunbathe. They had lazily agreed that they hadn't really wanted to sail anyway and, after having blown up two large air mattresses, had floated around the boat on the sparkling blue water. Rachel remembered it as a day made in heaven. Fish had leaped off in the distance, and there had been the occasional sound of a motorboat passing by. When they'd had too much sun, they'd merely slipped off the air mattresses, cooled down in the water and then climbed back on. They'd talked idly about nothing in particular, at least nothing that she could recall that had any importance until that odd moment.

She'd drifted away and was slowly paddling back towards Christopher who was lying on his back, his eyes closed against the sun. Rachel hadn't been able to resist the mischievous gesture of splashing some water on his bare chest.

'Not nice,' Christopher said, not moving or opening his eyes.

'I was just checking to see if you were alive.'

'Barely.'

'Let me feel your pulse.' She took hold of his wrist which was dangling in the water.

'You're on vacation, doctor.'

His pulse was strong and rhythmic under her fingers. 'Surprise,' she said, 'there's still some hope for you.'

'Thanks.'

Rachel held on to Christopher's wrist as she lay her cheek down on the air mattress, feeling the air-filled canvas yield to the weight of her head. Christopher turned his hand upwards so that their palms met and their fingers entwined. For a few minutes, they drifted together.

'Rachel?'

'Mmmm.'

'Have you ever thought about children?'

She hadn't lifted her head to look at his face. 'You mean, having them?'

'Yes.'

'Sometimes.' There was a pause and it seemed that Christopher had no intentions of pursuing the conversation any further. Rachel still didn't lift her head, but she added, 'What about you?'

'Sometimes,' he said.

And that was it. They had gone on drifting in the sun, the heat making Rachel feel lethargic and finally dizzy. When that happened, she announced that it was time to go back to their cottage before she burnt to the crisp she'd already become. Christopher had smiled at her and agreed. They had returned the sailboat to the marina, gone to the cottage, showered and made love, silently and with an unusual ferocity. Then they'd had a memorable seafood dinner at a nearby restaurant and watched a floor show with a moderately good comedian and half-a-dozen can-can girls. They had never mentioned having children to one another again.

When they returned to Washington, they occasionally got together with Harvey and Samantha. That relationship was running a different course than Christopher's and Rachel's. It was still on a friends-only basis, although it frequently threatened to turn into something else. What held it back from a full-fledged affair was nerves—Samatha's nerves or Harvey's nerves. They both had such a good time together that they alternated worrying what would happen if they became lovers. Samantha confided in Rachel; Harvey confided in Christopher. Both of them had had friendships ruined by sex.

'If Harvey and I don't make it in bed,' Samantha said one night as she and Rachel waited for the two men to park the car by a suburban theatre, 'then I'll lose him.'

'Coward. Look at me. I did as you suggested, I threw caution to the winds.'

They were standing under the awning of the theatre,

and Samantha gave Rachel a smiling look. 'You're positively glowing, you know.'

'Glowing?'

'Radiant—like a bride. That sort of thing.'

Rachel put on an innocent air. 'Christopher and I are having a wonderful summer.'

'Mmmm—and I'll bet the sex is great, too.'

'Jealous, Sam?'

'God, yes. The trouble with Harvey is that he doesn't seem like great lover material.'

Rachel put her hands on her hips. 'Sam, you know what I think?'

'What?'

'That you're afraid.'

'Me?' Samantha put on her tough act, tilting her head to one side and giving Rachel a nasty glance. 'Afraid of what?'

But Rachel wasn't put off. 'That you and Harvey might be compatible in bed. Then you won't have any excuses.'

'Excuses for what?'

'For getting serious.'

Samantha sighed. 'How did you know?'

'Sam, I can read your mind.'

Samantha glanced away from Rachel as if she could avoid that mental telepathy and then sighed again. 'The last time I got serious, I was married, pregnant and then divorced.'

'It might be different this time.'

'But neither Harvey nor I can stop thinking about it. We talk about marriage all the time, the pros and cons, the good parts and the bad parts. And when I'm feeling positive, he's feeling negative and vice versa.'

'Why not just relax?'

'We both know it can't be anything casual. Honest to God, Rache, it was a lot easier in the old days when you met a guy, fell in love and married him. Now, we have so many alternate lifestyles, we can't decide what to choose.'

'It seems to me,' Rachel said, 'that you're making it more complicated than it is.'

'Are you kidding? With two houses and two kids and two cars and . . .'

'. . . and two dishwashers and two sets of dishes,' Rachel said laughing.

Samantha threw up her hands. 'I know. I know. It's ridiculous. But listen, you and Christopher are lucky. At least you don't have to worry about the future.' And then she turned as Harvey and Christopher arrived.

But Rachel gave Samantha a look of surprise before moving to Christopher's side. She'd never thought of her non-future with Christopher as lucky. She had considered it as a burden, a sad weight that they carried with them, its presence adding poignancy to everything that they did. It hadn't occurred to her that their lack of future might, on the other hand, be a release; giving them freedom, unleashing them from the pressures of commitment. They were able to take each moment as it came without making promises that couldn't be kept or having dreams that couldn't be fulfilled. Lucky? Rachel wondered. Perhaps in an odd sort of way, they were.

When summer ended, Christopher's social obligations began again. The weather was unseasonably hot, and Rachel found that she was often too tired after a day's work to have sufficient energy to accompany him to cocktail parties. She had forgotten how much energy light-hearted conversation and small talk required, and she had also not realised the demands that would be made on Christopher. In the past, she and Christopher had gone to such functions and, because of his low status at the Embassy, they'd been able to stay together, enjoy the food and watch the people. But now, his position was such that a diplomatic affair had lost its element of fun. He and Rachel didn't go to be sociable, to meet other couples and to widen their circle of acquaintances. They went so that Christopher could complete his day's work. He had to make the rounds; shaking the appropriate hands, letting himself be seen and discussing business. He was apologetic, but he had to leave Rachel on her own while he circulated. She met some interesting people and was introduced to those whose faces adorned the front pages of *The Washington Post*. But their sociability was superficial, their interest in her waning when they realised that she had no political connections. She wasn't surprised by it, and Christopher understood when she said she'd rather not go.

Christopher was also obliged to have a number of parties of his own, and these were done with the help of two cooks and several waiters. Rachel stood by Christopher's side at the receiving line, acted as his hostess and was just thankful that she didn't have to cook for eighty-five or a hundred people. It was at these parties that she met some of the people from the Embassy. Lucy Solvano, for instance, arrived at one party in a gown so low that it made Rachel dizzy to contemplate her cleavage. She gave Rachel a smooth smile as she introduced herself and then proffered such a smouldering look on Christopher that, when she was gone, Rachel gave him an undignified poke in the side.

'And *who* was that?' she whispered.

'Jealous, my sweet?' Christopher said with a grin.

'Should I be?'

He batted his lashes at her in a girlish and flirtatious way. 'That's for me to know, and you to find out.'

'I will,' she said with a mock threat, 'you can depend on it.' And then smiled dazzlingly at another set of visitors.

It was at another one of Christopher's parties that she met Frank and Mary Newman. Mary didn't mix well; she stood over in one corner, sipping at the drink Frank brought her and staring at the clustered groups of people. She was a small, pretty woman but clearly unsure of herself, and Rachel took pity on her. She wandered over to Mary's side and struck up a conversation. It was during this that she figured out just whose baby Christopher had borrowed.

'I've met Lora,' Rachel announced.

'Lora? You mean, my Lora?' Mary stopped being nervous. Now, she was concentrating on Rachel.

'Yes, Christopher brought her to my office.'

'Was it *you* he wanted to play a joke on?'

'Yes,' Rachel conceded. 'I'm a paediatrician.'

It was like opening the door to a dam. The conversation flowed after that as Mary dug deep into the subject of her children. Rachel didn't mind being cornered that way; she was used to listening to mothers and accustomed to being asked for her professional advice on everything from growth patterns to teething pains. She heard how Lora had started walking and about Sean's nightmares. She smiled and nodded and noticed that Mary Newman was quite visibly relaxing. Her body didn't have that rigid look anymore, and she wasn't clutching her wine glass so hard that her knuckles were white.

Later that night, after everyone was gone, Christopher took Rachel in his arms, kissed her thoroughly and passionately and informed her that she was a saint for having taken Mary Newman under her wing.

'She's lonesome,' Rachel said, wrapping her arms around his waist.

'She's unhappy here and she wants to go back to Ottawa. As a result, she's driving Frank around the bend, and he's driving the rest of us with him.'

'Why?'

'He's not working up to scratch. Everyone's covering for him. I probably should have had him sent back to Ottawa last spring.'

'Why didn't you?'

'Why? Because of you.' He kissed her on the nose. 'Me?'

'I borrowed their baby, didn't I? How could I fire him after that?'

'It was a crazy thing to do.'

'Mmmmm.' Christopher was kissing her again and, for a while, they thought of nothing else.

Then Rachel said, 'Why not get her a small job?'

'What?'

'Mary Newman. Get her a part-time job at the Embassy to keep her busy and get her mind off her children. She has that syndrome I often see in mothers who spend too much time thinking about their children. She's obsessed with them. No wonder she drives Frank crazy.'

'I never thought of that,' Christopher said, musingly. 'There might be a spot available in the Embassy library.'

'Problem solved,' Rachel said and tried to kiss Christopher again.

'Not so easily,' he said. 'She doesn't drive and I'll bet she won't be able to find a babysitter.'

Rachel gave it exactly two seconds thought. 'Simple,' she announced, 'you have a butler, a cook and a housekeeper. They all have relatives, and I'll be one of them would love a part-time job taking care of children.'

'Maybe.'

'Frank can drive Mary in with him when he goes to work, and she can take a taxi back.'

'I bet she'll balk at the expense.'

'Not when you pay for the taxi.'

'Me?'

'It's the least you can do,' Rachel said. 'And you can afford it.'

'She wouldn't take money from me.'

'Don't tell her. Have the taxi fare included in her pay cheque. She'd never know where it came from.'

'Rachel . . .'

'You could do it, Chris. What's the point of all your

power if you couldn't arrange something as simple as that?'

Christopher gave her a wry smile. 'I'd hate to meet you across a negotiating table.'

'Well,' she said, 'I do feel sort of responsible for Mary Newman. If you hadn't wanted to see me again, Frank would have been fired and she would have been safe and happy back in her home in Ottawa. Come on, Chris. Say you'll do it.'

Christopher pulled her close again. 'Slavedriver,' he whispered in her ear and then added in a suggestive tone, 'is there anything else you'd like me to do?'

'Well,' she said primly, 'now that you mention it . . .'

'Yes? Yes?'

'How about a love scene? You know, foreplay, intercourse, afterplay.'

'So,' he said. 'You want the whole thing.'

'No half measures.'

'No cutting the corners.'

'No cheating,' Rachel agreed solemnly.

Christopher heaved a mock sigh. 'A man's work is never done.'

'Never,' Rachel said with a smile and then, wrapping her arms around his neck, brought his lips down to hers.

September slipped into October and October into November. The huge maples and elms that had shaded the grounds of the house turned to the colours of the harvest, their leaves golden and orange. The summer's heat dissipated and was replaced by an autumnal briskness. The days were busy for both of them. Christopher had to fly to Ottawa for a week, and Rachel attended a medical convention in San Francisco. Autumn had brought a horde of children who were picking up germs from schoolmates. A severe stomach 'flu made the rounds, keeping Rachel and the other doctors in her office working round the clock for about two weeks. She was so exhausted from it that, at first, she didn't notice that Christopher was preoccupied, his mind often elsewhere. Then when it did occur to her that he was very silent of late and asked him about it, he merely said it was overwork, and she took it as that. Overwork was something Rachel knew about intimately. She could understand why he was withdrawn and too tired at night to make love to her as much as he used to.

But had she been less busy with her own professional concerns, she might have guessed that something far more serious was going on. As it was, Rachel didn't discover what was bothering Christopher until the night of the ambassadorial dinner. It was one of those glittering affairs where high-level Canadians visiting from Ottawa got to mix with Washington's élite. The guest list, which Rachel had seen in advance, included Secretaries and Under-Secretaries, several well-known journalists, two Presidential aides, five Senators and a Congressman or two. The Ambassador and his wife, both white-haired and distinguished, had hosted so many affairs like this that Rachel supposed they could do it with their eyes shut. They formed a receiving line of two and never missed a name or a connection; smiling, talking and looking as if greeting a newcomer to the ambassadorial residence was their favourite occupation. Of course, Rachel thought, it helped to have a full staff of help and an assistant hovering nearby to catch them before they made any gaffes.

Cocktails were served in the foyer and living room. Rachel sipped at her martini and wandered around, looking at the Oriental rugs and the walls hung with works of Canadian art. She peered into the dining room where five round tables, each sitting eight, had been set with white linen, gleaming goblets and silver. Fresh roses adorned each table, their petals soft beneath the flickering of tall white candles, and she could see the tiny place cards at each setting that indicated the name of the person who would sit there. And just to make sure that no guest would be confused before he or she entered the dining room, there was a chart by the door showing the seating arrangement. Rachel glanced at and saw that she and Christopher wouldn't even be sitting at the same table. She had been sandwiched between the Secretary of the Navy and a Canadian Member of Parliament.

Christopher was still standing by the fireplace in the living room, talking to the Canadian cultural attaché, Gary Reade, and Rachel headed back towards him. He had just bought a new suit, a dark blue with a faint white stripe through it and, as she drew closer, she admired the cut of the cloth and the cut of the man inside. Christopher, she thought smugly, was the best-looking man in the room. With a lover's air of possession, she put her arm through his, smiled at Gary and caught the tail end of a conversation that was to destroy, in a horrifying and abrupt way, every belief and every tender myth that she had nurtured about Christopher and herself.

'Have you decided about Rome?' Gary was saying.

She felt Christopher go rigid, his forearm stiffening beneath her hand. 'Not yet.'

'External wants you to go.'

'Yes, I . . .'

Rachel had a premonition, an awful certainty that made her throat so dry it felt as if she could barely speak. 'Chris?' Rachel asked, forcing a smile on her face. 'What's this about Rome?'

He started to speak but Gary interrupted him, his wide smile beaming at her. 'Didn't he tell you? The Ambassador in Rome had a heart attack and External is bringing him home. They want Chris to take his place.' He heaved a theatrical sigh. 'Some people have all the luck. *Bene, bene*.' And he kissed the tips of his fingers in an Italian fashion.

Rachel's hand moved away from Christopher's arm and she clutched on to her goblet. 'Rome?' she asked, her voice a croak.

Damn. Goddamn. She wasn't supposed to know, and now Gary had let the cat out of the bag. He hadn't wanted to worry her; he hadn't wanted to stop what had become the most cherished time of his life. And he didn't know; he just didn't know what to do. He'd been agonising about it for days, torn into pieces by the thought of leaving her.

Rachel understood everything now—the preoccupation, the silence, the less-than-frequent sex. It was a nightmare that was happening all over again, history repeating itself like a bad record that played the same lousy tune in an endless repetition. Christopher had done the same thing to her before, making a decision on his own and then pulling away from her emotionally, turning cold and aloof and distant. Even his face held that neutral look that she'd learned to hate ten years ago. Rachel wanted to scratch it off, she wanted to tear at the skin above to find the man below. But, of course, she couldn't; just as she couldn't scream or yell or cry. Not in this luxurious living room with its elegantly dressed guests all talking in subdued murmurs.

'Rome?' she asked again, her voice stronger, the anger in it perceptible.

Gary was looking alarmed, glancing from Rachel to Christopher and then back again. 'Excuse me,' he said and slipped away.

Neither of them were aware of his departure. 'I haven't decided yet,' Christopher said in a low voice. Rachel. Don't be angry. I thought we had four years; I thought we had all the time in the world to play and learn about one another. I didn't know the future was going to come rushing at us like a train on the wrong track. I didn't know my hand would be forced so quickly.

'I see.' She could see everything so clearly now, the dishonesty, the arrogance and the betrayal. And she had thought it was different this time. After all, there'd been no assumptions, no commitments, no pledges of undying love and devotion. But she *had* believed that there had been trust and caring and sensitivity. Well, she'd fooled herself and, in doing so, she'd been blind to what was really going on. So gullible. So goddamned gullible.

'Rachel.' Christopher glanced at the clusters of people around them. 'Can we talk about this later?'

'No.'

'Rachel . . .' The hurt in her eyes. It was cutting at him. He could feel it in his heart. He hadn't meant to do this to her. He'd thought to protect her, but instead he'd caused her pain. He wanted to take her in his arms, to say the right words that would ease the hurt, to kiss those brimming brown eyes. But he couldn't—not here, not in front of these people. He'd do it later, tonight, when they got home.

But Rachel was turning and walking away, putting the martini down on a side table and praying that she would get out of there without either breaking down or killing him. She could feel the tears pricking at the back of her eyes and, if there was one thing she didn't intend to do, it was cry in front of this elegant gathering and the man who had humiliated her once again. And, as for killing him, unfortunately there were laws against actions like that. She made her way through the crowd, knowing that Christopher was behind her and not caring that people were looking at them. The scent of roses was making her nauseous, and she passed by the Ambassador and his wife without seeing them.

'Rachel!' She was almost at the door when Christopher grabbed her wrist. 'You can't leave.'

'Oh, yes, I can.'

'Rachel, please. I promise we'll talk about it after the dinner.'

'It's too late.'

The maid who opened the door was now staring at them as if they were crazy, and Christopher began to get angry. 'Rachel, this is bad manners.'

'I don't care.'

He dropped her wrist then, and Rachel turned and walked out of the door. She knew that Christopher would feel his professional obligations so deeply that he wouldn't follow her. He had to mix with the guests, make polite conversation and do his bit to represent the nation of Canada. Well, she had no such responsibilities, and she didn't give a damn that she'd walked out of a dinner party without even the small gesture of saying goodbye to the host and hostess. She didn't intend to ever see those people again; she didn't intend to be part of Christopher's life again. He thought she would go back to the house and wait for him to return, but Rachel didn't intend to do that, either. Christopher would be occupied for the next two hours at the very least and, by the time he was finished, she would be long gone.

CHAPTER NINE

THE North Carolina beach wasn't friendly on this November day. The sky was grey with scudding clouds, and the wind seemed to have driven the ocean into a frenzy. The waves crashed against the beach, the dark water turning to a white froth that spewed high in the air. Above Rachel's head, the seagulls swirled in large circles. They associated people with food, and they followed her down the beach, waiting to scavenge whatever she left behind. Their cries were high and lonely sounding, and they made Rachel feel even sadder than she already was. She had thought a walk down the beach would ease the soreness she felt inside, but neither the walk, nor the wind, nor the water was having that beneficial effect.

She jammed her hands inside her jeans' pockets and hunched her shoulders in her windbreaker. Well, no one had promised her a rose garden and, in expecting one, she'd fooled herself into thinking that she was entitled to more than her share of happiness. She had thought she could have everything; a successful career, enough money so that she wouldn't have to ever count the pennies and the companionship of a man who loved and cherished her. For a while, it had seemed that she was blessed by the gods, but it hadn't lasted. In her heart of hearts, Rachel wasn't surprised. Shocked, yes. In pain, yes. But surprised, no. She didn't really believe in happy endings. They only happened to other people, not to her.

Take Samantha, for example. Rachel had gone to see her the night of the ambassadorial dinner. She'd taken a taxi to Christopher's house, quickly packed her clothes and, taking her own car, had driven to Samantha's.

168

She'd felt a desperate need for a friend's support and comfort. What she'd found was that she was a welcome but awkward third wheel. Not that Samantha wanted her to feel that way. She and Harvey offered her a drink, some food, and money if she needed it. They were also willing to be sympathetic listeners, but it was clear to Rachel when she'd arrived that she'd interrupted a lovemaking session. Both Ellie and Harvey's daughter were being babysat at his house, while he and Samantha were exploring that unknown side of their relationship.

Although the lights were blazing in the house, Rachel had been forced to ring for what seemed like ages before the front door opened, revealing Samantha in disarray. Rachel had apologised profusely, but Samantha had ushered her in and hovered around her like a mother hen with a lost chick. Harvey had come out of the bedroom in due course, looking appropriately concerned. They had treated her as if there was nothing else they would have rather done on earth than entertain her, but Rachel was too sensitive not to catch the undercurrents; the looks, the small smiles, the touching here and there. It was apparent that Samantha's love affair had blossomed into all it had promised to be.

Despite their objections, she had left and checked into a hotel for the night. She hadn't planned on staying with Samantha; she didn't want Christopher to find her until she'd had a chance to think. And the next morning, she'd called Molly at the office, said there was a family emergency and caught a plane to North Carolina. She knew that Christopher had high-level meetings in Washington for the rest of the week and, even if he suspected that she was at her mother's, he wouldn't be able to follow her. And if he 'phoned her? Rachel had no intentions of being available. All she wanted was the soft and soothing presence of her mother. Call it crawling back to the womb. Call it anything you like. Rachel didn't care if running to Phyllis was the most childish thing she'd ever done. She hurt so badly she had to do it.

But even Phyllis wasn't truly available to her. Rob was also visiting, and it was evident to Rachel that he was courting her mother. They were far less demonstrative than Harvey and Samantha, but Rachel could see what was brewing beneath the surface. For years Phyllis had insisted that Rob was only a friend, but it had all been a charade, a way to save face. And the swinging bachelor seemed ready to settle into something stable. Rob might have cautioned Rachel against deep relationships, but he seemed to have every intention of delving into one himself. It seemed to Rachel that no matter where she went for solace and hiding, she ran into lovebirds and their billing and cooing made her own misery that much harder to bear.

'Rachel!'

She turned and saw her mother walking to her, her hair blown back in the wind. Rachel thought that Phyllis was ageing more gracefully than any other woman she knew. She'd let her hair grow since she moved to the beach so that it hung straight and grey-streaked down her back. It didn't make her look odd; it made her look girlish in an attractive sort of way. She was already slender and petite, and the length of hair added to the image of a woman growing young rather than growing old. Today she was dressed in a heavy cable sweater, a pair of old cords and a scruffy pair of sneakers.

'Rachel! Wait up.'

Rachel stood there as her mother caught up with her. 'If it's a 'phone call from Chris, the answer is still the same.'

Phyllis smiled at her, and they began walking again. 'It was Christopher and I told him that I didn't think you'd changed your mind.'

'I haven't.'

'He's in distress, Rachel.'

'That's his problem.'

'Mmmm.' Shrewd blue eyes assessed her. 'I see.'

'But I'm not angry with him anymore—not the way I was.'

'Oh.'

'Well,' Rachel said brightly, trying to change the subject. 'Where's Rob? I thought you two couldn't bear to be separated.'

Phyllis actually flushed. 'Now, now. We're not as bad as all that.'

Rachel put her arm around her mother's shoulder and gave her a hug. 'I'm only teasing. And I'm pleased, I really am. I think you two should have been married years ago.'

Phyllis gave a happy laugh. 'Rob wasn't ready years ago.'

'What I want to know is if you had your eye on him all along and have just been biding your time until he came around?'

'It's funny,' Phyllis said reflectively, 'how it happened. He was your father's closest friend and, even after his death, he remained loyal. He couldn't think of going out with his best friend's widow. On the other hand, I think I realised that I was in love with Rob when you were . . . oh, about ten.'

Rachel shook her head in astonishment. 'That's a long time to pine for someone.'

Phyllis shrugged. 'By that time, I'd convinced myself I wasn't Rob's type. He liked glamorous women and,' she glanced down at her creased cords and laughed, 'I don't quite fit the bill.'

'Rob used glamorous women as window dressing—strictly for show. I think he had a yen for you all along.'

Phyllis had a small, secret smile. 'So he says.'

'So what will you do? Move back to Washington?'

This time it was Phyllis who looked surprised. 'Of

course not,' she said. 'Did you think I would? I love it here.'

'But what about Rob?'

'He's willing to commute and, besides, he'll be retiring in a few years.'

'Will he want to live here?'

'It's here or nowhere,' Phyllis said calmly. 'If he loves me, he'll have to come here. I waited for him in Washington long enough.'

They walked on, and Rachel contemplated her mother's strength. Phyllis knew what she wanted out of life, and she wasn't going to let anyone get in the way of her dream. For as long as Rachel could remember her mother had longed to live on the beach and paint. But she'd had a daughter to raise and a livelihood to earn, and for years she'd been a dutiful mother and the sole support of the family. It wasn't until now, when she was close to sixty, that Phyllis had been able to realise that dream. She had her cottage overlooking the ocean and a workroom full of light and paints and canvasses. Her ambition didn't extend to fame, glory or money, but simply to have an outlet for a creativity that had been stifled for years. Rachel could see that not even Rob would ever be able to budge her from it.

It struck her then just how much she and her mother were alike. She had the same stubborn streak and the same need to make her dreams come true. She'd wanted to be a doctor and had sacrificed a love affair and years of her life to achieve that diploma. And, even now, she would not give up her practice for anyone or anything. Not to go to Rome with all its exotic glamour. Not for Christopher, the man that she loved. Rachel knew that she'd never be happy as an ambassador's wife, standing at Christopher's side greeting guests and playing that diplomatic role. She had her own sense of creativity that had nothing to do with art or music or literature. Her talents were tied up with medicine and diagnosis and an instinctive caring for the smaller members of the human race. She was, Rachel supposed, an artist in the healing of children, and it was an art she could never willingly give up.

'We're a lot alike, aren't we?' she asked.

And Phyllis understood perfectly. 'Yes,' she said, 'we are. It's not an easy way to be, is it?'

'No,' Rachel said wryly. 'It requires suffering.'

They turned around and began walking back to the cottage. Rachel lifted her head to the wind, letting its fingers tug wildly at her hair. She'd spent hours on this beach, walking for miles in the mist with the ocean pounding in her ears. And during those hours, she'd worked hard at sorting through her emotions. Anger had eventually yielded to understanding, and understanding to compassion. The hurt still remained, and she still blamed Christopher for causing it but, for the first time in years, Rachel thought she had a clear view of the past.

'Remember how you told me that once I wanted Chris to be a father to me?'

'Yes.'

'At first I thought you were crazy, but the more I looked back at the past, the more I decided you were right. I wanted an awful lot from Chris when I was twenty. I needed all sorts of things from him; protection and love and nurturing—in a daughterly sort of way. And I didn't want to see him as someone who might have problems of his own. That would have ruined my image of him. And I think he fell, unconsciously, into the role I set for him. He was dominant because I wanted him to be that way, and he kept his own needs to himself. I put too much pressure on him to be perfect.'

'It was a tall order.'

'But I don't need a father any more,' Rachel said.

'No, you don't.'

'But Christopher doesn't really know that. And what he did—not telling me about the Rome posting—

was ... well, part of being fatherly. He was protecting me again.'

'That's possible.'

'I mean, at first, I thought it was sheer dishonesty, but I'm not sure about that anymore.'

'Perhaps the subject upset him so much that he couldn't even voice it aloud to you.'

Rachel quickly glanced at Phyllis. 'I hadn't thought of that.'

'As you've just pointed out—he's only human.'

'What happened isn't precisely a repeat of the past,' Rachel spoke slowly, as she tried to express her thoughts in words. 'The external circumstances seem the same, but the internal ones are different. He should have told me, he should have shared the problem with me, but he didn't. And, although I ran away like I did the last time, it's not the same either.' Phyllis was silent, and Rachel gave her an anxious look. 'I haven't fallen apart, have I? Not like I did ten years ago?'

This time it was Phyllis who put her arm around Rachel and gave her shoulders a motherly squeeze. 'No, it's quite different this time.'

Rachel knew that she would return to Washington, but not to Christopher. There seemed no point in continuing something that had no immediate future. Their affair was like a short-lived play whose curtain was now ringing down on the very last and very final act. She'd enjoyed it while it lasted, but she didn't want to drag out the agony of separation. She would go back to her apartment and back to work. She would return to her former life as Dr Rachel Sims, paediatrician and occasional woman about town. Oh, she knew it wouldn't be easy living alone, and she was going to mourn Christopher and their relationship deeply and with pain, but it would pass. The days would turn into weeks, the weeks into months, the months into years, and it would pass. Rachel had lived through such grief before. She gave a great sigh and glanced up at the gulls that wheeled overhead.

'You told me to be strong,' she said, 'but I didn't know if I could be.'

'I had faith.'

'Did you?' Rachel asked, stopping and looking at Phyllis.

'You're *my* daughter, aren't you?'

They were both smiling when Rob's voice came faintly over the roar of the wind and the waves. 'Phyllis! Rachel! Are you going to stay out there forever?'

Both women looked towards the cottage and saw him waving at them from its doorway. Even in this rugged setting of angry sea and sky he was dapper, his chino pants perfectly pressed, his pullover band-box new, a silk ascot tied at the opened neck of his shirt.

'Are you sure about him, Mom?' Rachel murmured.

And again Phyllis knew exactly what she meant. 'If he loves me,' she said drily, 'he'll learn to live with a few creases.'

Christopher was in a private meeting with the Ambassador. They were both seated on a couch that sat at one corner of the Ambassador's office. His was the only room in the Embassy that was adorned with an Oriental carpet and original art, and it was designed to make visitors feel comfortable. But the ambiance wasn't working for Christopher. He felt damned awkward sitting there, sipping at his coffee and listening to the Ambassador lay out, in the starkest terms, what would happen if he didn't take the Rome posting.

'I can't say it would absolutely ruin your career at External, Chris, but it sure as hell wouldn't help it.'

'You mean, they wouldn't offer me another ambassadorial posting?'

'Look, the posting is a prize, and they offered it to you because you deserve it and because you're single. They figured that if anyone would be easy to move in December, it would be you. If you turn it down, they won't think so readily of you next time—if there is a next time.'

Christopher winced. He'd come to the Ambassador for advice because he was a man who, despite his reputation for diplomacy, didn't mince words. And, although Christopher wasn't surprised by those words, he was discovering that he didn't much like hearing them.

'I don't know what to do,' he said heavily.

'You'd be crazy not to take it. Rome is a major post.'

'I know.'

'Well, you've got a few more days.' The Ambassador straightened up, and Christopher knew that the private part of their meeting was over. He hadn't expected any sympathy, and he hadn't received any. But then the Ambassador didn't mollycoddle staff. He expected the Embassy to run smoothly, and he didn't believe that either he or his underlings should allow personal matters to interfere with professional duties. Needless to say, it was an attitude that had enhanced his career immensely. Christopher had no idea what effect it had had on his family. 'We've got that trade meeting now, haven't we?'

'At Commerce.'

'Ready for it?'

Christopher patted the loose-leaf binder on the seat next to him. 'I've got the briefing book right here.'

'Okay, we'll talk about it on the ride over there. Let's get going.'

The trade negotiations were some of the toughest Christopher had ever been involved in, and he returned home that night with his shirt sticking to his back and his leg muscles feeling as if he'd run a marathon. He was also in the foulest mood of his life, disgusted with himself, with Rachel, and with his job. He felt like breaking something or someone with his bare hands, but being a civilised man, he took a less primitive route towards easing his misery. He ordered a scotch on the rocks from Finnegan when he walked through the door and, while that was being made, he got out of his suit and took a long, hot shower. It wasn't until later, when he was sitting in his living room, sipping at his drink, and idly perusing his mail that he found the letter from Rachel. To his surprise, his fingers trembled slightly as they tore open the flap of the envelope.

Dear Chris,

Please accept my apologies for walking out on you before the dinner. It was the wrong thing to do. I should have stayed and talked out the problem of the Rome posting with you. And I'm also sorry that I refused your 'phone calls in North Carolina, but I desperately needed the chance to think things through and to try to figure out what would be the best for the both of us.

I've decided to return to my apartment and to pick up my life where it had stopped when you came into it again. I don't think it would be wise for us to see one another. You'll be leaving for Rome, and I have a career that requires a great deal of care and attention. A prolonged parting would be painful and destructive.

This is harder for me to write than I thought it would be, but Chris—I had a wonderful time while it lasted, and I only wish it could have gone on forever. But life seems to have chosen different futures for us, and I don't see any possibilities that we will ever be together again. Unless, perhaps, there is another life, beyond this one, in which the circumstances are different. But that's only whimsey, of course.

I hope that Rome turns out to be everything you've worked for. You go with my blessings and my best wishes.

And she had signed it, Love, Rachel.

Christopher put the letter down, took a large swig of his whisky and leaned his head against the back of the couch. It was a graceful letter. A superb example of expository prose and an altogether fine missive. It let the axe fall gently, the severing of their connection done in the most ladylike, genteel fashion. What had he expected? Ranting and raving fury? A letter full of abusive words and derogatory phrases? Like—Chris, you blew it. You handled me with the kind of finesse one expects from a bull in a china shop. Your arrogance is breathtaking and your actions are unforgivable. I never want to see you again because I can't bear to lay eyes on you. Because that would have been closer to the truth.

'Goddamn it!' he roared and Finnegan came scurrying in from the kitchen.

'Sir?'

'Sorry,' Christopher mumbled and then, 'How about another scotch?'

'Certainly, sir.'

The second scotch went down smoothly but it didn't make Christopher feel any better. He hated himself for what he had done to Rachel. He had abused the trust she had placed in him. He had treated her love as if it were nothing, a bit of garbage, an old piece of paper he had crumpled in his hand and discarded because it lacked importance. He had taken the premise of equality on which they were building their second relationship and destroyed it utterly and completely. And he had no one to blame for that destruction but himself.

He had thought he was being so goddamn chivalrous in keeping the Rome posting to himself. The idea of having to leave Washington in a month's time was so horrible that he'd protected Rachel from it, keeping it secret, worrying over it, turning it over in his mind a million times, and trying to find the answer that would make both of them happy. At least that's what he thought he was doing, but instead he was treating a grown woman like a child who must be kept innocent from the unsavoury facts of life. It was no wonder that she'd been furious and insulted.

And, of course, that wasn't the only reason. Christopher looked deep into the amber depths of his scotch and then deep into himself. He'd turned macho, not wanting Rachel to see his unhappiness and despair, not wanting to get emotional in front of her. Hell, he hadn't even wanted to admit that he loved her so much that he was actually considering turning down the Rome posting and thereby ruining his career as a foreign service officer. During the two weeks that he alone had known about the posting, Christopher had felt so emotionally vulnerable that he'd done everything possible to protect himself. Instead of crying, he'd become preoccupied. Instead of making love, he'd turned over and gone to sleep. And, instead of letting himself feel any pain, he'd hurt Rachel as badly as a man can hurt a woman.

Christopher finished the second scotch and was about to ask Finnegan to get another when he thought of his father and grimaced. Liquor held no answers and getting stinking drunk wouldn't solve his problems. He leaned over, picked up Rachel's letter again and gazed at it. It was all very simple. He had two choices; to go to Rome and leave the only woman he'd ever loved or to stay and give up the only career he'd ever known and wanted. The half measure of staying on at the Embassy if he did turn down the Rome posting didn't appeal to him. It was then only a temporary position with no future to it. On the other hand, if he stayed, he wouldn't have a job either—at least, not for a while. Rachel would have to be the sole support of the family. Christopher smiled ruefully to himself. The choice was now more focused. The Canadian Ambassador in Italy or a kept man?

Well, it all really boiled down to one thing. Could he live without Rachel? Could he live without her smile, those laughing brown eyes, the body, lovely and soft, that meshed with his so perfectly? Could he bear to return to his old life, the one in which solitude lay so heavy on his soul that he spent his evenings seeking the casual flesh of strange women? Or return to that old personality of his—the one that was sombre and serious, unhappy and morose? And giving up Rachel also meant giving up the only chance he would ever have to become part of a family. Christopher didn't see himself marrying or having children with anyone else, and it had come to him recently that he didn't want to grow old without children. He wanted a son and a daughter, a home, a wife—the whole domestic scene he had once rejected out of hand.

I don't think it would be wise for us to see one another. Well, Rachel had decided that she could live without him. That realisation rankled more than he thought it would; the old ego was a little bit too fragile to bear the weight of knowing that Rachel was quite willing to sacrifice him for her career. For a second, Christopher felt the old anger surge up, but then it died away. And why shouldn't she? he thought. Her work was meaningful and important, and it supplied her with a vast resource of human emotion. Dealing with children and parents kept her in touch with the feelings of love, of caring, of nurturing, of happiness and of misery. It wasn't abstract like his work. She didn't have to write memos about politics and economic theory. She didn't deal with cold facts and numbers, with bureaucratic red tape, with strutting politicians and diplomats who had a grandiose sense of their own significance in the cosmos. Rachel simply tried to heal children.

On the other hand, he could be as cynical as he liked about the foreign service, but its lure for him was deep and genuine. And the prospect of Rome glittered before him like a jewel, the fulfilment of dreams he'd held for so long that they clung hard and fast. Rome meant an enormous and extremely flattering promotion. It meant being in the thick of European politics. It meant moving in circles of influence, power and prestige. Christopher drank the last drop of his scotch and stared into space, his teeth unconsciously clenching together so hard that the muscles moved in his jaw.

Rome or Rachel?

The lady or the tiger?

A rock or a hard place?

Rachel was hemming a skirt when the doorbell rang that evening. She stood up, but her movements were cautious. Although she'd written to Christopher, saying that they shouldn't see one another again, she hadn't been sure he would agree. But a week had gone by since the letter had been mailed, and there'd been no 'phone call and no unwanted visitor banging at her door. Part of her, the romantic part that cherished the notion that Christopher would give up everything for her, had been deeply disappointed. Rachel, of course, was well aware just how adolescent and unrealistic this part of her was. The other part was far more pragmatic. It understood that she'd never see him again and that life wasn't a bowl full of cherries and that, like any fully grown person, she had to bear the burden of her own decisions. That part of her reigned in daylight when pragmatism was necessary and deserted her at night when the silly romanticism took over and made her cry.

Still, Rachel knew that she had done what was right for her, and the visit to her mother had been like a stamp of approval. She could never have been happy giving up her practice to go to Rome with Christopher, and she would have made his life miserable if she had. No, it was better this way. Far better. And that tiny bit of irritating romanticism would eventually die of starvation, leaving her nights calm once again and her heart at rest.

There was another ring at the door, louder this time.

'Coming,' Rachel called. She was only in a bra and

slip, and she pulled on a bathrobe, tucking the cord around her waist. Then she opened the door slightly so that the chain lock still held and peered through the crack.

A deep voice said, 'It's the mad seducer.'

'Oh, Chris,' she said.

'Damn, you saw through my disguise.'

They were both smiling when she undid the chain lock and opened the door, but their smiles immediately faded as Christopher entered. He was dressed casually in dark slacks, a dark shirt and a beige windbreaker. His hair had been tossed by the wind, and Rachel had the sudden urge to smooth it down. But instead she fell back on an awkward politeness. 'Won't you come in and sit down?' she asked.

Christopher looked at her; at her hair tumbling down her back, at the opened throat of her bathrobe where a tiny pulse beat in her flesh, at her bare toes peeking out from under the hem. 'No,' he said.

Rachel was taken aback and didn't know what to say. Finally, she found another question. 'Did you get my letter?'

'Yes.'

There was a pause. 'Did . . . you read it?'

His grey eyes were dark, stormy. 'Yes.'

She clenched her hands together. 'Chris, I'm sorry. I didn't mean to run away like that . . . I shouldn't . . . it wasn't right . . . it wasn't . . .'

But Rachel didn't have a chance to finish what she had intended to say. She was in Christopher's arms then, and he was kissing her forehead, her eyes, her temples, her mouth. His lips moved on hers, forcing them to part, and their tongues met. It was a kiss of passion, of desire and of urgency. And it expressed all the emotions that had buffeted them both: unhappiness, frustration, the despair of separation. Rachel forgot everything for the moment but the feel of Christopher against her, his body hard, his arms strong, his mouth so sweet on hers. She loved him and she wanted him. Nothing seemed to matter, not the hurt of his betrayal or the unhappiness she had suffered during the past weeks, not the decision she had made or her determination to forget that he ever existed. All her intentions evaporated in a warmth that spread deep within her, and her fingers moved to touch and arouse him, tucking under the edge of his windbreaker and pulling at his shirt so that it came loose from his slacks. She felt the coarse springiness of his body hair, and the hardness of abdominal muscle. She felt . . .

'Rachel.' Christopher pressed his hand against hers so that it couldn't move any longer. 'We have to talk first.'

But she could feel him trembling and knew that he wanted her. 'It's all right,' she whispered.

'The Rome posting . . .'

She gave her head a vehement shake. 'I don't care if you're going to Rome. I want to forget about it. I . . . I want to go to sleep with you.'

'But I'm not,' he said.

She was confused. 'You're not what?'

'Rachel, I'm *not* going to Rome.'

She stepped back then, her eyes wide and startled. 'You're not?'

'No. I've resigned from the foreign service.'

They stared at one another for a moment, and Rachel could see just how hard and painful that resignation had been. Christopher was thinner, his skin stretched taut over his cheekbones, and there were lines of strain around his mouth and nose. The magnitude of his sacrifice hit her then and, when she spoke, her voice was hardly above that of a whisper. 'Oh, Chris. Are you sure?'

'Yes.'

The tears that she had not cried at the ambassadorial dinner nor shed during all those hours of pacing the North Carolina beach now filled her eyes so that her vision became misty. She blinked and her eyelashes went spiky and the tears began to spill over, rolling in drops down her cheeks. 'Chris . . .' she cried helplessly.

And then he was kissing her again so that both their mouths could taste the salt of her tears. 'I love you,' he said. 'God, how I love you.'

'But, Chris, your job . . . career . . . Rome . . .'

He hushed her then, placing his finger across her trembling lips. 'It's all right,' he said softly. 'What I learned this past week was that I needed you far more than I needed anything else. Rome would be nothing without you. My job would be worthless if you weren't there. Rachel, I have a horrible confession to make.'

'What?'

'I don't think I can live without you.'

Tears filled her eyes again. 'Is that so terrible?' she said softly.

He gave her a wry smile. 'You can live without me.'

'Not well,' she said, 'not happily.'

'But you can . . .'

'Chris . . .' and this time it was Rachel who put her finger to his lips, 'it's not a weakness. Really, it isn't. *I* couldn't live without *you* ten years ago. Perhaps, relationships are always like this, always unequal. Maybe, ten years from now, I'll need you more than you need me.'

His smile was even more rueful. 'You should have been the diplomat.'

She put her arms around his neck. 'I love you,' she said and started to kiss him when he shook his head.

'There's a catch.'

'There is?'

'I've joined the ranks of the unemployed.' He paused and then gave her a lopsided smile. 'Rachel Sims, will you have me?'

Her arms tightened around his neck, her wet cheek placed against his. 'I'll have you,' she said, and then added with a gentle ferocity. 'I'll have you forever.'

*   *   *

Lucy Solvano was walking through Bloomingdale's and wishing that she hadn't blown her entire pay cheque already when she spotted Christopher Blake walking hand-in-hand with a very pregnant woman. They looked quite happy; he was smiling down at the woman and she was laughing at something he had said. She was a pretty woman despite the bulk of the baby she was carrying. Honey-brown hair tumbled down her back and, even from the distance, the delicacy of her features and the wideness of her brown eyes were visible.

For a moment, Lucy felt a pang of jealousy cut right through her. So, it was true after all. Christopher Blake had left his high-paying job and his promotion as Ambassador to Rome for a woman. His resignation had caused the Embassy to buzz with gossip and speculation for weeks. His secretary Margaret had been tight-lipped and sour, but they'd finally dug it out of her that, as far as she knew, he had no other job, no other prospects.

Cherchez la femme, someone had said. And, while they'd all laughed, a certain wistfulness had been in their laughter; each and every one of them imagining having a man love her so much that he'd abandon a successful career to be at her side. About a month after that, Margaret had announced that Christopher had got a job at the World Bank, but the news had not altered that very first and very romantic first impression.

Christopher and Rachel stopped a few yards from Lucy, shifted the packages they were carrying and then disappeared into the crowd. The image of them stayed in her inner eye until she willed it to be gone. What the hell did she care? she thought, giving a shrug. There's lots of fish in the sea. And then she tossed back the long length of her black hair and headed quickly to the dress department, ignoring the sad state of her bank balance and the budget she'd been so intent on following.

She suddenly had an intense craving for a new dress. Something that would make her look sexy. Something that would make her feel absolutely sensational. Lucy wasn't introspective enough to examine her motives any more deeply than that, but as she flipped through the dresses on the rack, she felt that aching emptiness that not even the most beautiful dress would ever fill. It was an emptiness that came to her at odd and un-acknowledged moments. When she felt vulnerable. When she was lonely. When she saw a man leaning over the woman he loved, his eyes looking into hers, his hand resting on the swell of her abdomen—gently and lovingly resting against the weight of his unborn child.

NEW LONGER HISTORICAL ROMANCES

You'll be carried away by The Passionate Pirate.

"I want that woman – and I take what I want."

And so the beautiful, headstrong Angelina Blackthorne is abducted by the very man who she held responsible for her father's ruin.

Alone and vulnerable, she falls victim to his ruthless desires.

Yet try as she might, she can't hate him as she feels she should ... in the way he so rightly deserves.

'The Passionate Pirate': available from 11th April 1986.

Price £1.50.

ROMANCE

Variety is the spice of romance

Each month, Mills & Boon publish new romances. New stories about people falling in love. A world of variety in romance — from the best writers in the romantic world. Choose from these titles in March.

RECKLESS Amanda Carpenter
MAN IN THE PARK Emma Darcy
AN UNBREAKABLE BOND Robyn Donald
ONE IN A MILLION Sandra Field
DIPLOMATIC AFFAIR Claire Harrison
POWER POINT Rowan Kirby
DARK BETRAYAL Patricia Lake
NO LONGER A DREAM Carole Mortimer
A SCARLET WOMAN Margaret Pargeter
A LASTING KIND OF LOVE Catherine Spencer
*BLUEBELLS ON THE HILL Barbara McMahon
*RETURN TO FARAWAY Valerie Parv

On sale where you buy paperbacks. If you require further information or have any difficulty obtaining them, write to: Mills & Boon Reader Service, PO Box 236, Thornton Road, Croydon, Surrey CR9 3RU, England.

*These two titles are available *only* from Mills & Boon Reader Service.

Mills & Boon the rose of romance